The Food Lovers' Christmas

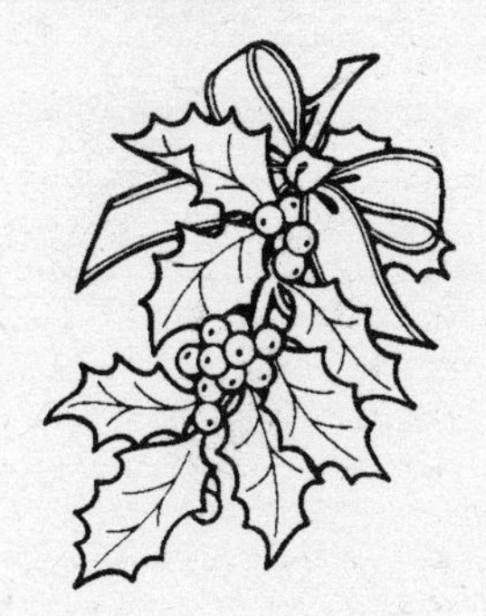

The Food Lovers' Christmas

WHAT TO BUY AND WHERE TO SHOP
FOR THE PERFECT CHRISTMAS

HENRIETTA GREEN

Ebury Press

First published in Great Britain in 1997

1 3 5 7 9 10 8 6 4 2

Ebury Press
Random House, 20 Vauxhall Bridge Road, London SW1V 2SA

Random House Australia Pty Limited
20 Alfred Street, Milsons Point, Sydney, New South Wales 2061, Australia

Random House New Zealand Limited
18 Poland Road, Glenfield, Auckland 10, New Zealand

Random House South Africa (Pty) Limited
Endulini, 5A Jubilee Road, Parktown 2193, South Africa

Random House UK Limited Reg. No. 954009

A CIP catalogue record for this book is available from the British Library

ISBN 0 091 85404 0

Typeset by SX Composing DTP, Rayleigh, Essex
Printed and bound in Great Britain by Cox & Wyman Ltd

Papers used by Ebury Press are natural, recyclable products made from wood grown in sustainable forests.

Contents

Foreword

We are delighted to be associated with Henrietta Green's latest guide for the discerning food lover, this time devoted to Christmas.

Port has long been an inseparable part of Christmas celebration. This supremely sociable wine, with its richness and warmth, represents the essence of Christmas entertaining. Plum pudding, Stilton cheese, mince pies, all kinds of traditional Christmas food, would not be the same without a glass of the greatest of all fortified wines.

However, as all food lovers know, port is not just a Christmas drink. There is a style of port for every season and occasion: the mellow and opulent old tawnies, for example, are perfect winter pudding wines but also make excellent summer drinking, served slightly cool. There can be no better summer aperitif than a glass of dry white port, served chilled with a plate of almonds or olives. And what more fitting way to mark an anniversary or special occasion at any time of year than to decant a bottle of a rare old vintage port.

Taylor's have been making the finest port wines for over three hundred years. Like many of the producers recommended in this book, we are a family company, dedicated to the quality of our wines and to passing on to succeeding generations the skills which have made Taylor's the greatest name in port.

We hope that our wines and Henrietta's excellent advice will help you create the happiest and most memorable Christmas ever.

Adrian Bridge, Taylor's Port

Introduction

There is one thing certain about Christmas – every year it comes around with clockwork regularity. Yet it still throws a lot of people into a state of panic. Of course it ought to be a time to enjoy ourselves. Apart from celebrating the religious significance of Christmas, we want to see friends and family, eat some jolly good meals, decorate the home, give or go to parties, and give or get presents.

I cannot claim that *The Food Lovers' Christmas* will solve your every problem - some families will never get on, no matter what. But as for what and where to shop, it certainly should. I hope you will use the book as a guide, follow its suggestions and generally let it take the strain. During the run-up to Christmas everyone can find shopping a nightmare, so I have focused on producers who not only stock excellent quality products but also offer a mail order or home delivery service.

You will find recommendations for every course for the Meal, with sources for alternatives if you don't want to serve a turkey or goose or if you are entertaining vegetarians. There's a breakdown of the best Christmas drinks, ideas for the days on either side including holiday standbys and what to serve at parties, Christmas treats from abroad and where to buy them in this country, solutions for presents for food lovers, and some interesting decorations.

As always, I have made my selection from the smaller speciality craft producers whose food offers taste, character and integrity. Although it may not always be cheap, it certainly represents value in terms of flavour and quality. Some of the producers are very small indeed, and others may have their products widely distributed, but all of them strive to provide the best and to offer an efficient and friendly service.

Although I have given a last order date, remember though it is not a guarantee that stock will still be available. So please order as early as you can to avoid disappointment - although I am certain everyone featured in the book will go out of their way to help you. Do try and give clear instructions about when you want delivery (some producers send by post, others by special delivery services); and if you are going to be out, state clearly where you want your parcels left. I have taken great care that all information was correct at the time of going to press, but as always I cannot accept responsibility for errors or changes that may have occurred since then.

All that remains is to thank my editors, Julian Shuckburgh, Margot

Richardson and Marnie Haslam of Ebury Press, Margaret Hickey for help with the drinks and Claire Clifton with decorations, Richard Busby whose suggestion it was to write this book, my many friends who have sampled and tasted the products with me and pronounced their opinions, and finally the producers themselves. Not only do I want to thank them for continuing to produce their excellent foods that make eating so much more pleasurable and exciting, but also for the time, trouble and patience they have devoted to explaining their products to me.

May I wish you all a very Merry Christmas and a Happy Successful New Year, and hope that, armed with *The Food Lovers' Christmas*, you really do enjoy yourselves this year.

Henrietta Green

Christmas Shops

As you leaf through the following pages, you may notice that I have not included many of our food shops. This has been deliberate: I wanted to guide you to the primary sources, the outlets from where the foods are produced. But these shops are useful and cannot be ignored altogether, so I decided to list the best of them here. As ever, London probably comes out tops (certainly with quantity), with the four food shops sited in the major department stores:

Fortnum & Mason, 181 Piccadilly, W1A 1ER (Tel: 0171 734 8040; Fax: 0171 437 3278)

Harrods, Knightsbridge, SW1X 7XL (Tel: 0171 730 1234; Fax: 0171 581 3946)

Harvey Nichols, Knightsbridge, SW1X 7RJ (Tel: 0171 235 5000; Fax: 0171 235 5020)

Selfridges, 400 Oxford Street, W1A 1AB (Tel: 0171 629 1234; Fax: 0171 495 8321)

These are all pretty good, offer delivery within the London area, have glossy catalogues and put together hampers and/or selections for their mail order service.

Smaller food shops within London worth seeking out are:

Bluebird, Sir Terence Conran's recently opened new food market, at 350 King's Road, SW3 5UU (Tel: 0171 559 1000; Fax: 0171 559 1111). Not only (and very flatteringly) will they be featuring some of Food Lovers' Christmas favourite products, but also all sorts of baked Christmas treats culled from abroad.

Clarke's, 122 Kensington Church Street, W8 4BH (Tel: 0171 229 2190; Fax: 0171 229 4564) is chef Sally Clarke's shop. They sell some fine own-made mincemeat, sensational chocolate truffles, various own-made chutneys and preserved fruits and other seasonal goodies. But they do not supply by mail order.

Felicitous, 19 Kensington Park Road W11 2EU (Tel: 0171 243 4050; Fax: 0171 243 4052) has very high tech design, well chosen products (I should declare an interest here as I helped with the selection), and a wide range of own-made food-to-go over the holidays.

Partridges of Sloane Street, 132-4 Sloane Street, SW1X 9AT (Tel: 0171 730 0651; Fax: 0171 730 7104) put together some interesting seasonal hampers.

Villandry, 170 Great Portland Street, W1N 5TB (Tel: 0171 631 3131; Fax: 0171 631 3030) has an accent on French produce.

Scattered over the country are several more which I must also mention:
Blar Ar Fwyd, 25 Heol yr Orsaf, Llanwrst LL26 0BT (Tel/fax: 01492 640215) has an excellent range of own-made jams, pickles and chutneys, as well as Welsh cheeses.
Chatsworth Farm Shop, Stud Farm, Pilsley, Bakewell Derbyshire DE45 1UF (Tel: 01246 583392; Fax: 01246 583464) puts on a pretty fine all-round show for Christmas.
James & John Graham, Market Square, Penrith CA11 7BS (Tel: 01768 862281; Fax: 01768 867941) is an old-fashioned grocer with traditional Christmas hampers.
Valvona & Crolla, 19 Elm Row, Edinburgh EH7 4AA (Tel: 0131 556 6066; Fax: 0131 56 1668) has a stunning range of Italian foods.
Stein's Delicatessen, Middle Street, Padstow, Cornwall PL28 8AP (Tel: 01841 532221; Fax: 01841 533566) is owned by TV chef Rick Stein, who also runs the Seafood Restaurant in the same town. I have just heard that this year he launches a range of hampers (oyster boxes actually) packed with own-made products and promising such delights as fish soup, rouille and pickled salmon. I haven't tried them yet, but if they are up to his usual standard they should be very good indeed.

The Christmas Meal

Starters

Alba Smokehouse

Kilmory, Lochgilphead, Argyll and the Islands, PA31 8RR

Tel: 01546 606400 Fax: 01546 606400

Contact: Mike Leng. Last orders 10 December. MasterCard, Visa. Delivery charge: prices include p&p.

There are many variables to take into account when it comes to smoking food, but Mike Leng seems to have taken them all into consideration. Sourcing as locally as possible, he places an emphasis on the buying of his fish. 'If you haven't got a good base raw product, you're struggling from the start.' Working from a modern unit on an industrial estate using Afos kilns, Mike aims to marry traditional techniques with modern equipment.

Salmon and trout are lightly sprinkled with sugar 'to take out the bitterness', then with salt; and finally wet-cured in a brine solution. Wary of over-smoking or 'kippering', Mike pre-smokes overnight with the fans off but with the minimum of smouldering wood to dry the fish, and then slowly builds up the heat over a further 12 hours to give it 'depth'. This way of smoking, developed through trial and error, would apparently have taken three to four days in an old-fashioned kiln. As for the end result, his smoked salmon is moist and chewy, a cunning balance of a light, sultry smoke and a rich fishiness. Sold in various sizes, ranging from 225g at £7.80 to a 900g whole sliced side at £25.50, it is a very pleasing product.

Hot-smoked salmon, Mike's favourite, is equally successful. Smoked as fully trimmed fillets on the skin, they too are moist and succulent with a light smoke, and struck me as similar to eating poached salmon with an extra edge. New this year, and incidentally winner of the Gold Award at the 1997 Scottish Hotel and Catering exhibition, is the Hot Smoked Cajun Salmon. Prepared in the same way as the plain version, it then has 'a real mixture of pepper, paprika, herbs and spices – but I'm not saying what' spread on top for a fiery finish before it is smoked. Both hot-smoked salmons come in 900g trimmed fillets at £25.50, or in packs of four portions at £11.50.

Mike also cures and smokes herrings for kippers, hot- and cold-smokes trout and hot-smokes scallops, queenies and mussels. A good present for any fan of smoked fish is his Connoisseur's Pack. It contains smoked salmon, smoked queen scallops, and mussels, two pairs of kippers and a tub of his cream cheese and smoked salmon pâté, and costs £30.

Brown & Forrest

The Smokery, Bowdens Farm, Hambridge, Nr Curry Rivel, Somerset, TA10 0DR

Tel: 01458 251520 Fax: 01458 253475

Contact: Michael Brown. Last orders: 18 December. Switch, MasterCard, Visa. Delivery charge: prices include p&p.

Michael Brown has been curing and smoking eels for over 15 years, and I reckon his are the best. As the natural habitats of the common or freshwater eel are rivers, ponds and lakes, it is vital they come from clean, unpolluted water. Michael Brown collects his from the upper reaches of the rivers Avon, Itchen, Stour and Test. 'They're all chalk streams, good clean rivers upstream with good feed.'

For smoking, the best of all eels are silver – mature – eels. Plump and juicy with a rich, succulent flesh the eel turns silver in autumn as it is ready to start its extraordinary, exhausting journey downstream and on to its breeding grounds in the faraway Sargasso Sea. 'You know intuitively when they're going to run. Usually it's with a deluge of rain after a dry spell. Then they run downstream with a vengeance. They're caught on racks straddled across the rivers, because if the river is in full spate you can't get the nets out. The brown or younger eels have already hibernated, so what you catch is 99 per cent silver eel.'

Michael blast freezes the eels ('it's the most efficient and painless method of killing them'). He then has a supply of eels in prime condition throughout the year, and draws on his stock as and when he needs them. First he brine-cures them for two to three hours. 'Although you can dry-cure, I always brine them because I learned the trade in Germany and that's how they do it over there. I also believe you get a more even uptake of salt.' Then he hot-smokes them over beechwood to cook them right through. A whole eel weighs 1½lb and costs in the region of £9.25 per pound. It yields enough to feed six as a starter but you have to do the skinning and filleting. Far easier is to buy the neatly cut, skinned fillets weighing 4oz and 8oz that feed two and four and cost around £5 and £9.25 respectively. To kick off the meal, Michael recommends eating them simply seasoned with freshly ground black pepper and a squeeze of lemon to cut their richness.

With 'the bits that don't fit the fillet packs', Michael makes a sumptuous smoked eel pâté that he describes as 'more of a pâté mousse, with plenty of loft' (a technical textile term meaning airy or standing up proud). Made with smoked eel, single cream, horseradish, lemon and black pepper folded into yet more whipped double cream, an 8oz pot costs £4.50. It makes an ideal first course served with toast and watercress salad. Failing that, you could try his hot-smoked salmon steaks that have been marinated in salt, vinegar, brown sugar, soy sauce, garlic, ginger and more than a dash of sherry. Best eaten slightly warmed so the juices run, they are succulent with a well-judged spiciness.

Butley Orford Oysterage

Market Hill, Orford, Woodbridge, Suffolk, IP12 2LH

Tel: 01394 450277 Fax: 01394 450949

Contact: Robert Jenkin. Last orders: 15 December. No credit cards. Delivery charge: prices include p&p.

There is a constant debate about the various merits of farmed versus wild smoked salmon. Poorly farmed salmon can run to fat, which is not only unpleasant to eat but can cause it to leech oil after smoking. On the other hand, a bruised wild salmon that has flailed itself to death in a net will not cure well, nor will a fish caught high up in the river after weeks of starvation (salmon do not feed in the rivers). What these relative points highlight is the importance of the condition and quality of the fish as well as the methods of curing.

Butley Orford Oysterage cure and smoke both farmed Scottish or wild Irish smoked salmon. I have to say that by and large they choose their fish very carefully. The wild is particularly impressive. Lightly cured, with the merest hint of mild smoke, it is lean and easy textured. To eat it is a joy, like biting into butter, and it slips down the throat with resounding waves of pearly fish. With farmed smoked salmon costing £12.20 per pound, and wild at £16 per pound, I leave it up to you which to choose.

Deeside Smoked Salmon

Headinch House, Dinnet, Aboyne, Grampian, AB34 5NY

Tel: 01339 885304 Fax: 01339 885304

Contact: Fergus Cumming. Last order: 10 December. No credit cards. Delivery charge: p&p extra.

What makes Fergus Cumming's smoked salmon so unique is his deep and serious understanding of the nature of the fish. He knows when wild salmon are in peak or poorer condition, and he operates on a tiny scale, so he is able to adjust and tailor his curing and smoking to suit each and every fish. 'You should always leave a salmon at least a day or two – depending on the weather – to go through rigor mortis', he told me. 'They are stiff when caught, but as the muscles relax they loosen up. Then you can start to cure.'

He smokes both farmed and wild salmon. The latter is either netted at sea and bought in Aberdeen, or caught in the river and bought wherever possible. Sea-caught fish, Fergus notices, can sometimes be softer than river fish. They tend to have harder, tougher muscles, 'no doubt from fighting the currents as they swim upstream'. A wild salmon can be richer in oil ('sometimes it just oozes oil in the kiln'), whereas a farmed fish is drier but fatter, with reserves of fat around its belly. As Fergus says, 'one thing is certain: if you start with a good fish, you will end up with a good smoked one'.

The fish are salted in a pure dried vacuum salt, similar to a table salt, which he feels is best for curing. The whole sides are washed down and put in the cold kiln, which is then fired up using oak sawdust and chippings as fuel so that it gently smoulders. 'If it goes to flame, I'm in trouble.' Whole sides will stay there for as much as nine or ten hours. Then he turns off the kiln, and the fish are left for a drying period until, going by feel, he knows they are ready. Fergus smokes to order, selling both farmed or wild smoked salmon as whole or sliced sides weighing 3lb and costing £18 and £21 respectively.

By choice, he would always smoke wild salmon, provided of course that the fish was in good condition to start with; but such fish are becoming more elusive. 'Farmed is improving in quality, but there is still a difference in texture. It is generally much softer textured, but then wild salmon has had to work for a living.'

Fletchers of Auchtermuchty

Reediehill Deer Farm, Auchtermuchty, Fife, KY14 7HS

Tel: 01337 828369 Fax: 01337 827001

Contact: Nichola Fletcher. Last orders: 1 December. MasterCard, Visa.

Delivery charge: £9.95 standard, with smaller items sent by first-class post if cheaper; orders over £90 carriage free.

Apart from farming red deer, Nichola Fletcher writes cookery books, specialising not unexpectedly in venison and other game. She also produces various interesting venison-based products.

Favourite is the venison carpaccio. Made using a single muscle butchered from the haunch, Nichola dry-cures it in salt, sugar, pepper and spices for about ten days. Sold thinly sliced in 100g packs costing £3.65 (which feed about four), it has a tender texture and a rich resonance of game. I adore it as a first course drizzled with extra-virgin olive oil and a dash of lemon juice, and scattered with finely chopped flat-leaf parsley. Nichola also cures other cuts for about seven days in a mixture of salt, sugar, beer, juniper and root ginger brine, then sends these off for hot- or cold-smoking.

Also certainly worth a mention is her 'spoonable' venison pâté. Rich and smooth, it is made with venison liver, lots of butter, wine vinegar, eggs, breadcrumbs and seasonings. First she braises the liver, then pulverises it with the other ingredients to achieve the right texture, and finally pots it. Sold vacuum-packed in a 10oz carton costing £4.70, or a 12oz pottery dish ('nothing fancy, but something you could put on the table') costing £6.95, it is pleasantly mellow.

The Galloway Smokehouse

Carsluith, Newton Stewart, Dumfries and Galloway, DG8 7DN

Tel: 01671 820354 Fax: 01671 820545

Contact: Allan Watson. Last orders 12 December. Switch, MasterCard, Visa. Delivery charge: £3.60 per kilo, or £8 for any weight by carrier.

The Galloway Smokehouse is run by the forthright Allan Watson, who has very decided views on how to cure and smoke. 'There is a huge variation between the very good and the very awful. Everyone wants good smoked salmon, but all too often it disappoints. And what a lot of people don't realise is that it also makes a huge difference in how the salmon is cured and smoked. I cure and smoke for my taste. If customers don't like it, they can go somewhere else.' But they usually don't, as very good his produce is too.

Allan sees curing and smoking as: 'all about a balance between sugar, salt and smoke. The more salt you use, the more sugar it needs. If you don't use sugar, then you have to cut down on salt and smoke and it turns out very bland.' For a densely textured and an obvious – but not overly so – sweetness, well balanced with a marked woodiness, his salmon are dry-cured in straight salt for six to twelve hours. Then a dark syrup of molasses mixed with rum is ladled on top and left for a further twelve hours, and finally the fish is cold-smoked over whisky-impregnated oak sawdust from Grant's Distillery for 24 to 36 hours. This Christmas, for the first time, he will have wild as well as farmed Scottish salmon, 'but customers must realise that I buy in the wild as fresh from June to September and freeze it for smoking later. Not that freezing takes anything away. But they should know you can't have smoked salmon from fresh wild salmon at that time of year. Prices for farmed salmon promise to be around £21 a kilo for a whole unsliced salmon or £25 a kilo for sliced sides or packs, with wild smoked salmon costing around an extra £2.50 per kilo.

Allan also cures and smokes large sea trout in exactly the same way and sells it sliced in 250g packs costing £7.50. Smaller freshwater trout are hot-smoked, as are his succulent Barbary duck breasts.

Inverawe Smokehouses

Taynuilt, Argyll and the Islands, PA35 1HU

Tel: 01866 822446 Fax: 01866 822274

Contact: Rosie Campbell-Preston. Last orders: 12 December. Switch, MasterCard, Visa. Delivery charge: prices include p&p.

Apart from curing and smoking various fish, such as trout, wild and farmed salmon, and eel from Loch Awe, Robert Campbell-Preston of Inverawe Smokehouses also prepares trout caviar.

I love it. Little (they are smaller than salmon eggs) bright orange balls, they pop in your mouth with a mild saltiness and a delicate taste of fish. Use them as a starter, treating them exactly as you would 'proper' caviar. That is to say, serve them chilled, turned out into a glass bowl, with slices of lemon, a little chopped dill (it works better than parsley), chopped hard-boiled eggs, and slices of toast. Or you could spoon them onto blinis (buckwheat pancakes, available from most good delis), spread with sour cream mixed with chopped dill.

The process of extracting the roe from the trout is laborious, and it has to be done between October and December before the fish start breeding. If you leave it later, the roe turns hard and tastes bitter. Once it is removed, Robert freezes some for the rest of the year and works on the remainder immediately. First he griddles the eggs out of the membrane, cleans them, matures them overnight in salt, then pots them in 65g glass jars which cost £15.65 for three. It may sound simple enough to make, but it took Robert three years to get the technique right and he reckons he is still learning.

Hard-boiled Trout Caviar Eggs

To eke out the trout caviar, try this recipe for an easy starter that can be prepared well in advance of the meal.

Take one hard-boiled egg per person and carefully cut off the top. Spoon out the egg and chop it quite finely. Add enough sour cream and/or mayonnaise to moisten the mixture and to bind it together, then mix in a dash of dry white wine, some chopped fresh dill, chopped spring onions, and season with plenty of cayenne pepper – but go easy on the salt. Pack this egg mixture back into the empty shells, then decorate the top with a mound of trout caviar, finishing with a sprig of fresh dill. Serve in an egg cup with slices of toast.

James Baxter & Son

Thornton Road, Morecambe, Lancashire, LA4 5PB

Tel: 01524 410910 Fax: 01524 833262

Contact: Bob Baxter. Last orders: 18 December. MasterCard, Visa. Delivery charge: prices include p&p.

The potting of fish, meat or cheese is one of the great traditions in British cookery. Whatever is to be potted, the process is more or less constant: the ingredient, minced, pounded or whole (in the case of shrimps), is seasoned with spices, pressed into a pot and sealed in clarified butter.

Bob Baxter's family has been potting shrimps for 200 years. His is the sixth generation. Once the family ran their own boats, had a wet-fish shop and employed a large staff, but Bob is now content to buy in his shrimps, sell them from his freezer centre and have Kathleen and Doreen producing about 500 pots a day in a small, neat kitchen.

The tiny brown shrimps are still processed in the same time-honoured way. Caught in the sandy estuaries of Morecambe Bay from the traditional 25-foot boats, they are cleaned and boiled at sea in sea water, peeled by the fishermen's wives and delivered to their door within 36 hours of being caught.

For the best of all potted shrimps, the peeled shrimps are kept whole (although some recipes suggest they are pounded) and lightly cooked in spiced butter to infuse with the flavours. Typically, Bob will not reveal exactly which spices he uses; but hazarding a guess, I would say he has stuck to the traditional use of mace and nutmeg. The shrimps are chilled, packed and sealed with butter into 2oz or 7oz pots which will feed one or three to four people respectively. The minimum quantity you can buy is ten 2oz pots for £29, or five 7oz pots for £46.

The ratio of butter to shrimps is one of Bob's great concerns. Some potters, he claims, put too much butter in with the shrimps or cover them with too thick a layer. His, I assure you, have copious quantities of moist, succulent, gently spiced shrimps that are marked by their sweet fresh nuttiness. Ideal as a starter for the meal, serve them with brown toast, a slice of lemon and cayenne or black pepper.

Loch Fyne Smokehouse

Clachan, Ardkinglas, Cairndow, Argyll and the Islands, PA26 8BL

Tel: 01499 600217 Fax: 01499 600234

Contact: Andy Lane. Last orders: 13 December. MasterCard, Visa, Amex, Diners. Delivery charge: £5.95 on any order.

Loch Fyne is particularly rich in plankton, which makes for fat, juicy oysters. And although it is a sea loch, the oyster beds are sited far up the loch so the waters have a relatively low saline content, making the oysters surprisingly sweet and not too salty.

Bought in as seed, the oysters are laid down in net bags on racks on the loch's shore. They take about two summers to reach a good size, and once harvested they are passed through a purification tank for 48 hours, before they are ready for the table. Although wild natives are to be found occasionally on Scotland's west coast, Loch Fyne Oysters grows mainly Pacific oysters, or *Crassostrea gigas* to give them the correct Latin name. Forget the myth about only eating them when there's an 'r' in the month; these elongated, cupped oysters can be eaten all year round, and are especially good at Christmas.

Hardened off by exposure to the elements at low tide, these oysters will not gape but stay firmly shut even when out of water, making them ideal for home delivery. Their usual weight is 90 to 105g – although a monster Henrietta (no relation) currently tips the scale at 675g – and they are sent out wrapped in seaweed in a wooden panier to keep them fresh, with one dozen costing £7.80. And if the idea of opening them daunts you, Loch Fyne can also supply a *clic huitres*, a cunning French gadget that holds the oysters while you slide in the knife.

The Loch Fyne Smokehouse (same business, same location – just a different name) dry-cures farmed salmon in salt and soft brown sugar for about 12 hours, then cold-smokes it for six to eight hours. Many people, myself included, compare theirs to a London smoke; at its best, it does have that yielding, mild texture and soft buttery flavour. It is sold in 250g and 500g packs at £13.70 and £7 respectively, and you can also buy a whole side for £19.75 or a sliced side for £25. They also smoke mussels, cods' roe, trout, *Bradan Rost* (Gaelic for roast salmon), and cure *gravadlax*. All these more than acceptable as simple, easy starters.

Mooreland Foods

Vost Farm, Morley Green, Wilmslow, Cheshire, SK9 5NU

Tel: 01625 548499 Fax: 01625 548606

Contact: John Ward. Last orders: 10 December. Switch, Delta, MasterCard, Visa, Amex, Diners. Delivery charge: £6.50 for overnight carriage. Minimum order £25.

A couple of generations ago, Mooreland Foods was purely a ham and bacon curer (see page 67). Now its range has expanded to include all manner of poultry, meat, game and fish; and I believe the Wards number among Britain's subtler smokeries.

The smoked chicken breasts are superb: light, delicate, with a great succulence, they are cured in a gentle mixture of salt, honey, brown sugar and fresh garlic, then hot-smoked over oak chippings mixed with beech in one of Mooreland's traditional smokeholes. Excellent as a starter with a mixed leaf salad and a light olive oil dressing, I have served them several times and they are always admired. Sold as individual breasts weighing 6oz, they cost £2 each.

Equally interesting are the lean, meaty smoked duck breasts. Here a cure of salt, honey, garlic, ginger and soy sauce is used as a foil to the inherent richness of the duck. These I also serve as a starter, shredded into a bowl of thread noodles tossed in a soy sauce dressing, or with thin slices of ripe mango. They are sold as whole breasts weighing 10oz, and cost £5.50 each.

The Wards have also developed a range of sausages or, as they call them, charcuterie. There are various fresh sausages, including pork with coriander and garlic, and a robust Cheshire *saucisson sec* made with chopped coarse pork, garlic and wine that is filled into natural skins, soaked in brine and air dried for eight to nine weeks. They cure and hot- smoke pork loin for a mild *kassler*, and cure topside of beef in red and white wine, bay leaf and cloves for a *bresaola* that packs a salty punch.

Mrs Tee's Wild Mushrooms

Gorse Meadow, Sway Road, Lymington, Hampshire, SO41 8LR

Tel: 01590 673354 Fax: 01590 673336

email: 106225.2141@compuserve.com

Contact: Brigitte Tee-Hillman. Last orders: 21 December. No credit cards. Delivery charge: p&p extra.

For a quick and easy first course, why not buy a jar of Mrs Tee's mushroom confit? Really more a salad than a conserve, it is made with generous slices of different wild mushrooms, including chanterelles both *gris* and *jaunes*, ceps and oyster. These are cooked in a white wine vinegar and flavoured with various herbs, with port and truffle oil added. Nicely textured and with plenty of flavour (if perhaps slightly on the sharp side for some), the confit can be added to various mixed leaves or served as a crostini on thick slices of grilled country bread brushed with olive oil. A 200g kilner jar costs £7 and feeds four, and a 350g jar at £11 will easily satisfy seven.

The Old Smokehouse and Truffles

Brougham Hall, Brougham, Penrith, Cumbria, CA10 2DE

Tel: 01768 867772 Fax: 01768 867772

Contact: Rona Newsom. Last orders: 5 December. No credit cards. Delivery charge: prices include p&p.

Rona Newsom is particularly keen on using local produce to develop interesting products. She cures and smokes the local breed of sheep (see page 136) and has recently started smoking char. Char was once found in great quantities in nearby Lake Windermere, and is similar to trout in both looks and flavour. Indeed, potted char was such a delicacy that it used to be sent down by the overnight train to Fortnum & Mason.

Caught only rarely in the lake, it is now being farmed outside Wigton, from where Rona gets her supplies. A whole fish weighs about 8 to 9oz, and is first briefly brine-cured in salt with lemon juice, sugar, garlic and onion, then cold-smoked for a couple of hours and finished by hot-smoking to cook it through. The result, sold in packs of four costing £17.75, is a fish moister than trout, with a compact but soft-textured flesh and a subtle taste.

To make potted char, Rona suggested flaking the fish with a fork and mashing in softened butter, pepper, lemon juice and a sprinkling of cayenne. And if you want to keep it you must seal it with clarified butter.

Rannoch Smokery

Kinloch Rannoch, Pitlochry, Tayside, PH16 5QD

Tel: 01882 632344 Fax: 01882 632441

Contact: Leo Barclay. Last orders: 12 December. MasterCard, Visa. Delivery charge: £1.60 per 250g; overnight delivery on request.

Leo Barclay concentrates on smoking local produce that includes wild red deer shot on the surrounding estates. First it is hung for about a week to develop its flavour (if Leo lets it go for longer, some customers 'complain about a really gamey taste'). He butchers the haunch (leg) into the three main cuts: silverside, topside and thick flank, for 'decent slices of meat from the three main muscles'. These he brines into a mixture of muscovado sugar, salt and 'three secret ingredients' for about three days, and hangs them to dry for about 48 hours. Both these processes are done at a controlled temperature which Leo considers 'really counts for the flavour and texture'.

Next comes the smoking, which takes about three days. Leo favours a heavy cold-smoke, and uses oak chips from whisky barrels. Finally the venison is thinly sliced and vacuum packed, either plain or marinated in oil and herbs, or in olive oil and mixed wild mushrooms. He picks these himself, dries them slightly if they are a little wet, as they sometimes can be, then marinades them in an Italian olive oil ('extra-virgin is too heavy and pervasive'). The wild-mushroom-infused oil, complete with tiny bits of the mushrooms, is poured over the meat. The result is delightfully delicate, a mix of gentle woodiness with mild gaminess. Sold in 100g and 250g packs, expect to get about ten to twelve slices per 100g ('enough for four to five as a starter'). Costs range from £4.90 per 100g for the plain to £6.15 per 100g for the wild mushroom-infused venison.

Leo also hot-smokes whole grouse ('it's the most magic way to treat an old bird, as it tenderises them'), whole pheasant, chicken, and duck breasts which he sells ready sliced.

The Scottish Gourmet

Thistle Mill, Biggar, Strathclyde, ML12 6LP

Tel: 01899 221268 Fax: 01899 220456

Contact: Gillian Bell. Last orders: 8 December. Switch, MasterCard, Visa, Amex, Diners. Delivery charge: £6.85; over eight items, carriage free.

I must make one thing clear: the Scottish Gourmet is a food club, and you have to join in order to have access to its products. Membership costs £14.45 for three years, and entitles you to receive the monthly newsletter from which you can order. What is also unusual about the Scottish Gourmet is that it sends out vacuum-packed cooked dishes. Prepared in its kitchens to a high standard, using quality ingredients (they are very proud of how they source), the dishes are a boon for food lovers in a hurry or unable to cook. And while I have to admit I have not tried any of their food, I have heard nothing but good reports from friends who have.

For a Christmas starter, on offer is Meg Dod's oyster soup, made to the authentic 19th-century recipe. Its base is a bouillon made from oyster shells, then cream, beaten eggs, whole oysters and a pinch of nutmeg are added. A carton to serve two costs £4.78, and to serve four, £8.88. Last year it also offered soup *à la reine* (also known more prosaically as white soup), and a deep red beetroot and tomato soup. If soup is not to your fancy, you could try garlicky (sic) mushrooms: a mixture of wild and cultivated mushrooms cooked with garlic, tomatoes and onions folded into a bay leaf flavoured bèchamel sauce, at £6.47 for 450g. Or Springbank pâté, described as 'pure luxury and richness', that contains goose and duck livers, truffle peelings, malt whisky, cream, butter and fresh herbs, and costs £9.89 for 225g.

Seasalter Shellfish

The Harbour, Whitstable, Kent, CT5 1AB

Tel: 01227 272003 Fax: 01227 264829

email: seasalter@compuserve.com

Contact: Elaine Kirkaldie. Last orders: 22 December. MasterCard, Visa.

Delivery charge: prices include p&p.

If Christmas is the time for indulging ourselves, then what could be better than oysters? They go down a treat, either with a pre-meal glass of champagne (see page 104) or as the actual starter. Seasalter Shellfish, a direct descendent of the old Seasalter and Ham Fishery Company with premises at Whitstable harbour since 1893, send them all over Britain packed in the old-fashioned wooden baskets.

The good news is that they do have smallish quantities of the wild-caught Native Whitstable oyster, the *Ostrea edulis*. Because of their rarity – a recent problem with disease, over-fishing and water pollution – they do not come cheap. One dozen – the minimum quantity sent out – of Number Ones (the largest) costs £26, and two dozen £38; but aficionados say there is nothing to beat them for flavour.

On the other hand, you may actually prefer the Pacific oyster *Crassostrea gigas*, which has been officially re-named as the European cultivated oyster by, I think, the EU. Some say it is coarser textured and less juicy and sweet, but probably (and sadly) I do not eat them often enough to be able to tell the difference. Anyway, these now EU fully approved oysters cost £22 for two dozen (the minimum order), £26 for three dozen and so on.

At the bottom end of the scale – in price rather than necessarily in flavour – are the own-hatched and farmed Manilla clams, which are a snip at £5 a kilo which will give you about 30 pieces. These, I suggest, you treat as you might do mussels and steam them in white wine, garlic and chopped parsley. All Seasalter's shellfish are passed through purification tanks over a 48-hour period, and sent off by overnight courier.

Summer Isles Foods

Achiltibuie, Ullapool, Highlands and Islands, IV26 2YG

Tel: 01854 622353 Fax: 01854 622335

Contact: Keith Dunbar. Last orders: 7 December. Switch, MasterCard, Visa. Delivery charge: prices include p&p.

In what must be the smokehouse with one of the best views in Britain, overlooking the hump backs of the Summer Isles scattered in the sea, Keith Dunbar smokes a range of fish.

One of his specialities is salmon. He uses mainly farmed fish, and cures them in a sweet brine of salt, rum, molasses and boiled-up juniper berries for about eight hours. Opinions seem to be divided on whether a dry-salt or brine cure is the more effective. Keith prefers a brine, feeling it offers him more control and a greater subtlety of flavours. The salmon is smoked for up to 20 hours over oak shavings from the sherry casks supplied by a local whisky distillery, and the result is a mellow, rich fish with that melt-in-your-mouth texture. It is sold sliced in 225g packs costing £9.90, with discounts available for more than one offer item going to the same address. Keith will also supply whole sides, either sliced and laid back, or unsliced.

Wild salmon and farmed sea trout are prepared in the same way, and there are also hot-smoked salmon steaks, cut across a boned-out fish for a 4 to 5oz slice. These are brined and hot-smoked 'to cook them through', then lightly dusted with tarragon for an interesting depth of flavour. Sold at £9.50 per pair, they weigh 250 to 300g each.

Tideford Foods

Higher Tideford Farm, Cornworthy, Totnes, Devon, TQ9 7HL

Tel: 01803 712276 Fax: 01803 712388 email: tideford@shines.swis.net.

Contact: Diana Cooper. Last orders: 15 December. No credit cards. Delivery charge: £6 for up to 10kg.

Tideford Foods is based at Higher Tideford Farm, a picture-postcard setting in the South Hams. From here, in a kitchen unit converted from an old barn, Diana Cooper cooks up a range of ready prepared foods.

Most successful of these are her soups, which arrive in hermetically sealed kilner jars giving them a shelf-life of between 14 and 28 days (depending on the ingredients). Made with fresh vegetables 'that as far as possible are organic' and an own-made vegetarian stock as the base, the recipes change according to the season. Winter offers a seasonal Stilton and pear; Thai pumpkin; spinach and chestnut; or parsnip and ginger. These are obviously own-made soups, quite rough and ready, with a chunky texture (Diane makes a point of not over milling them), but good well-rounded flavours. Prices range from £3.20 for a 500ml jar (to feed two generously) up to £8.75 for a 1-litre jar which gives eight ladlefuls.

Main Courses

Turkey

I know what I expect from my Christmas turkey. Appearance-wise, it must be well proportioned with a plumptious well-rounded breast for plenty of white meat and with a blemish-free, unbroken skin. When it comes to flavour, some people may think of turkey as supplying no more than a background to all the accompanying stuffings and sauces; but I demand that it has a pronounced character all of its very own.

Bearing in mind that the turkey is a game bird, I look for a definite gaminess: a clear, clean-flavoured flesh overlaid with a dusky earthiness. And it must have a good length of flavour. With some turkeys the flavour evaporates as soon as you chew, and all you are left with is cotton wool. Ideally the more you chew, the more the flavour deepens and intensifies.

We all like our turkey moist, although this is trickier to control. To some extent it does depend on how you cook it. Sometimes, and usually in the case of butterballs or intensively-reared forced turkeys, the flesh is actually too moist. It can be slimy or, just as bad, so wet and rubbery that it almost bounces off the tongue like a released rubber band. No, what I want is dense and relatively firm meat with plenty of 'give', but not, however, too much so that the flesh splits into shards and becomes stringy. Believe me, it is a fine balance.

Various factors – breed, feed, rearing conditions, age, slaughtering, plucking, hanging, transportation – affect the eating qualities of a turkey, and for the best of all turkeys each and every factor has to be right. What you should look for is a slowly grown turkey fed on a cereal diet (no fish meal or animal protein to taint the flesh). As with all animals it should be killed as humanely as possible to avoid stress; and if it is to be hung uneviscerated it has to be dry-plucked rather than plunged into hot water and plucked by machines.

As a rule of thumb, allow 450g (1lb) per guest. Depending on how hungry (and greedy) everyone is, you should have some left over for Boxing Day.

Eastbrook Farm Organic Meats
Bishopstone, Swindon, Wiltshire, SN6 18PW
Tel: 01793 790460 Fax: 01793 791239
email: eastbrookfarm@compuserve.com
Contact: Deborah Archer. Last orders: 5 December. Switch, Delta, MasterCard, Visa. Delivery charge: £10 for orders under £35; £8 for £35–75; £4 for £75–150; over £150, carriage free.

Helen Browning of Eastbrook Farm is one of the leading lights of the organic movement in Britain. All her meat – beef, lamb, pork and even veal – is reared to Soil Association standards.

At Christmas she also has organic white and bronze turkeys to sell. Fed an 80 per cent organic, fully vegetarian diet of cereals and pulses supplemented with soya as protein (which is not allowed to come from genetically modified sources), these are healthy free-ranging birds with plenty of access to the outdoors. They cost around £9 per kilo.

This year Eastbrook Farm also has about two hundred Norfolk Black turkeys that manager Tim Finney describes as 'super organic'. What makes them unique is that they come from a breeding flock. Every other turkey grower buys in his birds as poults; these turkeys mate, lay eggs, hatch them and rear their young. 'They run as a large family. They are free-range – utterly so. They live in a roomy, straw-lined barn with their grazing area outside. Every morning they are let out and, unlike any other commercial flocks, actually fly there. At dusk, they fly back home. Don't ask me why they don't fly away, as I can't tell you. But they don't. This is a rarefied way of treating them. It represents a completely integrated life system.'

As for the eating qualities of these turkeys, Tim has no doubts. 'Their diet is good. They exercise. They're slaughtered at five months old, so they will have developed great flavour. And they're hung uneviscerated for ten days. I am totally convinced they will have great flavour.' They certainly do not come cheap; but it is reassuring to know that they have lived a 'natural' life. For some, this is a small price to pay.

Kelly Turkey Farms Ltd

Springate Farm, Bicknacre Road, Danbury, Chelmsford, Essex, CM3 4EP

Tel: 01245 223581 Fax: 01245 226124

email: kelly_turkeys@compuserve.com

Contact: Paul Kelly. Last orders: 18 December. MasterCard, Visa. Delivery charge: £10 per bird.

After several years of hard work improving and selecting from the best birds, Paul and Derek Kelly have developed the Kelly Bronze. The Rolls Royce of turkeys, it is a mixture of the flavoursome but keel-breasted Norfolk Black and the Cambridge Bronze lightly seasoned with the compact Rolstead White. The Kellys are confident they have a turkey with just about everything going for it. 'It offers a full flavoured, densely textured meat, marbled muscle meat and the good fat cover which is essential for moistness. And there is ample breast mass so you get plenty of white meat. It's a slow maturer so you really do get optimum flavour. It also matures to a range of sizes which means that even if you order a small bird it will have been grown for the same amount of time as a large bird so it will have the same deep flavour.'

According to Paul, one of the true tests of a turkey is when you eat it cold. And I have to say that – hot or cold – his Bronze birds have a lingering deep flavour, a fine succulence and punchy gaminess. 'This,' he explains, 'is because our birds are slow-growing, retain a certain amount of fat and, of course, are hung. The problem with birds improved from modern stock is that all their flavour has been bred out of them. They are lean, fast growing and exceptionally good converters of food into muscle (flesh). But they have absolutely no taste.'

I should mention the Bronze's appearance. Apparently, and I find this hard to believe, customers are sometimes put off by the tiny brown feather stubs that can be left in the skin after dry-plucking. I think this designer stubble makes them look cosy and old fashioned, but if you are used to a pearly white supermarket skin I can see it may take a little getting used to.

A free-range Kelly Bronze comes in a range of weights from 3 to 13kg, costing £21 to £59. You can either buy them direct from the Kellys, or they will put you in touch with other Kelly Bronze growers and stockists around Britain.

Roast turkey

'My mother,' says Clarissa Dickson Wright, 'on her path to perfection, devised a recipe which has given me headache-free Christmases ever since.' Here it is:

1 large turkey; 450g (½lb) butter; salt and black pepper
Stuffing 1: combine sausage meat and chestnuts, salt and pepper.
Stuffing 2: combine onions, breadcrumbs, parsley, thyme and celery or lovage seed, salt and pepper and a dash of cayenne. Cook together in plenty of butter.

Stuff your bird with Stuffing 1 at the breast end, and Stuffing 2 in the body cavity. Place on tin foil, season and smear the bird with butter. Wrap in the foil and cook at 180°C/350°F/gas mark 4. Allow 15 minutes per pound if under 6.8kg (15lb), and 10 minutes per pound if over this weight. About 20 minutes before the end of the cooking time, open the foil and fold back. Sprinkle with flour and baste. Zap up oven to 230°C/450°F/gas mark 8 and allow to brown. Serve with all the trimmings.

Peele's Norfolk Black Turkeys
Rookery Farm, Thuxton, Norwich, Norfolk, NR9 4QJ
Tel: 01362 850237
Contact: James Graham. Last orders: 8 December. No credit cards. Delivery charge: about £15 per bird.

This year food purists may decide to opt for a Norfolk Black turkey, one of the original and oldest breeds in the country. James Graham runs a flock of 200 breeding hens and 70 stags of four bloodlines started by his grandfather in 1880. They are, more or less, unimproved, which means that they will have the advantages of an intense gamey flavour with the attendant disadvantage of the leaner, longer shape of the game bird.

Not surprisingly, James Graham disagrees that its old-fashioned conformation works against it. 'My birds are longer legged with a long, angular breast rather than the shorter, wider breast of the modern hybrid birds. But they still offer plenty of breast meat as it runs along the whole length of the breast.'

As the true Norfolk Black is a slow grower, taking far longer than the modern breeds to reach maturity, James starts production in May. He raises the birds either free range or in pole barns (you can specify which you want to order and will be charged the same price). Fed on a drug-free, grain diet with field beans for protein and oats 'to give them bloom and a good fat finish', a hen bird weighs 7 to 12lb, and a cock 18 to 22lb. The weight gap in between is filled with Cambridge Bronzes bred onto his Norfolk Blacks, and he also takes these birds on to a weight range of at least 22lb; and he is very proud that all his birds mate naturally 'with no tinkering about'.

The birds are dry plucked, hung uneviscerated for seven days, and come oven ready. Prices range from £2.40 per pound for small birds to £1.70 per pound for the heaviest weights.

Norfolk Blacks get their name from their black feathers. No matter how carefully they are hand plucked, a few stubs, or little black pits, can get left behind under the skin. This does not affect the taste or texture of the bird, but in case you did not already know I am warning you about what some people may consider to be an off-putting appearance.

Piper's Farm

Cullompton, Exeter, Devon, EX15 1SD

Tel: 01392 881380 Fax: 01392 881600

Contact: Peter Greig. Last orders: 18 December. Switch, MasterCard, Visa.

Delivery charge: minimum order £40; £10 carriage charge.

Dedicated followers of *The Food Lovers Guide* will know that Piper's Farm won Best Butcher in the last edition, and no doubt will be relieved to hear that their high standards of excellence still prevail. Peter and Henrietta Greig, ably assisted by Ann Wilson, run the business with all the right priorities. They favour traditional breeds for optimal flavour; enforce strict animal welfare standards; rear all animals extensively; and hang their meat and poultry longer than most to tenderise and intensify its taste. Their butchery, which includes a full range of traditional cuts, their own style of Continental cuts and boned-out and stuffed joints, is first rate.

For Christmas, they grow Kelly Bronze turkeys (see page 28) in small groups of no more than 50 birds on various farms dotted in and around the Culm Valley. The flocks are free range in the true sense of the word: when I visited, admittedly on a sunny day in late autumn, they were all suitably unstressed, pecking around in the orchard. Peter assured me that his other farmers keep their turkeys in the same conditions. All the birds are fed a grain-only feed, supplemented with peas for protein, and are grown for 26 weeks. Hung for three weeks for a buttery tenderness, they are sold as oven-ready dressed birds in a weight range of 12lb to 25lb, and cost between 3.09 per pound and £2.60 per pound depending on their weight; but the smaller they are, the more they cost per kilo or pound.

Peter also sells two stuffed turkeys, both using a chunky, well-textured stuffing of chopped apricots, hazelnuts, fresh apples, ham, turkey meat, and onions flavoured with mixed herbs and lemon juice made on the farm. The first is a neck-stuffed turkey which comes as a whole bird with its neck generously stuffed. This is available in the same weight range as the oven-ready birds, but costs between £3.32 and £2.92 per pound.

The second version is a boned and stuffed turkey. Here, the whole turkey is boned out, trimmed, stuffed and then rolled and sewed up. Smaller sizes, where the carcass is split in half lengthways, look like a ballotine or a plump neck pillow, while larger sizes – which come from whole birds with their drumsticks still firmly attached – actually look like reassembled turkeys. They are sold blast frozen and vacuum packed. One pound will feed two people generously, and the weights of the birds range from 5 to 19lb. They cost from £5.90 to £5.45 per pound.

These are turkeys for inept carvers. You just cut through with a sharp knife for a slice of well flavoured turkey wrapped around the stuffing. With a good proportion of white to dark meat, they are relatively quick to cook: allow about 15 minutes to the pound. And because the birds have been so well hung, they will not shrink during cooking. It is a novel idea, and although traditionalists may balk at it, cooks seeking convenience and quality should snap them up.

Cooking times for a turkey

Cooking times are dependent on an accurate oven. For safety's sake, plan the timing so that, if all goes right, the bird will be ready one hour before the meal. This will give you leeway if necessary. When the bird is cooked, open the oven door to cool the oven, then put the turkey on a serving dish and put it back in the oven to keep warm.

Weight of bird when it is ready for the oven (regardless of whether it is boned, stuffed or empty)	4-5 kg 8-10 lb	5-6 kg 11-13 lb	6-7 kg 14-16 lb	8-9 kg 17-20 lb	9-11 kg 21-24 lb
Cooking time in hours at 180°C/350°F/gas mark 4			3-4	4-5	5-6
Cooking time in hours at 200°C/400°F/gas mark 6	2	2-2½			

From *Leith's Cookery Bible* by Prue Leith and Caroline Waldegrave (Bloomsbury)

Traditional Farmfresh Turkey Association
5 Beacon Drive, Seaford, East Sussex, BN25 2JX
Tel: 01323 899802 Fax: 01323 899583
Contact: Penny Jones

TFTA turkeys are easily recognised by the sign of the golden triangle, a gold-coloured swing ticket attached to every bird. This is a UK-wide group of some 42 turkey growers producing about 100,000 birds for Christmas grown to the standards set down by the Association. These include the birds' growing period (a minimum of 18 weeks); feed (a 100-per-cent vegetarian diet from six weeks onwards free of all growth promoters and antibiotics unless prescribed by a vet); plucking (all birds are dry-plucked); and hanging (they must be hung uneviscerated for a minimum of seven days to allow their flavour to develop. Remember, the turkey is a game bird and so needs to be hung to improve and develop its flavour). And every TFTA turkey must be sold fresh, never having been frozen.

But other areas are less well defined. Within the Association, there are two levels of welfare standards. Birds are either barn reared, where they are kept at a stocking density at or below that laid down by the Animal Welfare code, in naturally lit and ventilated buildings on a bedding of freshly topped-up straw or soft wood shavings; or they are free-range. In this case once the poults (baby turkeys) are eight weeks old, during daylight hours they must have access to open-air runs, mainly covered with vegetation, of at least 4 square metres per bird. The chances are that a free-range bird will have a superior flavour and texture. As one grower told me, 'exercise gives them a firmer flesh and the extra succulence from the grass goes right through to their wingtips'.

Some TFTA members grow White, others favour Bronze turkeys with the Bronze – or perhaps I should say the 'proper' Bronze – generally considered superior in flavour and texture. Here I must give a word of warning: some Bronze birds are the 'real' thing developed by Derek and Paul Kelly of Kelly Turkey Farms (see page 28); others are not. These are Bronze birds mixed with an ordinary fast-growing White so they give the appearance of Bronze with none of its eating advantages while costing as much as its slower growing, superior-textured cousin. Sadly, the TFTA does not regulate this – how can I put it tactfully?– aberration. So I do advise you to find out exactly what you are buying before you part with your money.

That having been said, a TFTA bird, from whatever welfare-standard and/or breed, will generally be better than most birds. Prices vary according to grower and the weight of the bird, but expect anything between £1.80 and £2.60, with an extra 30p per pound for a Bronze bird. For details of mail order, farm-gate sales or a butcher stocking one of their birds near you, contact the TFTA direct.

To carve the bird

When my parents were just married and the first joint was placed on their table, my father looked at my mother and my mother looked at my father. In his house his mother carved, in her house her father carved. Neither knew what to do. My father soon learned.

Carving does take skill, patience and – forgive me for stating the obvious – a sharp knife. Here are foolproof steps for tackling the turkey or goose that ensure that everyone gets their fair share of white and dark meat.

- Hold the leg by the end knuckle. Ease it away from the bird until you can see where to make a cut. Cut close to the body and twist it off. Carve the dark meat off the leg.
- Similarly remove the wing. If it is too large, cut it in half.
- Slice the breast meat from the half from which you have removed the leg and wing. Cut in thin slices, starting from the outside and working towards the centre.
- Repeat the process for the other side of the bird.

Do not forget to spoon out the stuffing from both ends of the bird. I did once, and no one had their stuffings until I came to dole out second helpings.

Goose

Every Christmas we always have the same discussion – what shall we serve for the Christmas meal? As a traditionalist, I favour goose; an old-fashioned bird, it is wonderfully rich and succulent with sultry, densely-textured meat. Another advantage is that it is almost impossible to over-cook, by which I mean that unless you leave it for hours and hours it never dries out, unlike a turkey. As for all the fat left in the pan,

I melt it down, strain it through muslin, pot it up and use it for cooking throughout the year. Goose fat is particularly effective for roasting potatoes.

Most geese on sale in Britain are from a Danish strain. Developed over several generations for a long lean bird, from several blood lines including the Embden, our white farmhouse goose and the Toulouse, it is thought to be the perfect balance of a good meat to bone ratio, well-textured flesh, and not too thick a fat cover. The actual flavour of the bird, however, is more likely to be affected by its feeding regime than its breed.

For the best of all geese, you need to make sure that it has been reared slowly (anything from five to seven months), allowed plenty of access to the outdoors to range on grass or, better yet, corn stubble for an even creamier flesh, and then hung for seven to ten days to tenderise the meat and allow its flavour to develop. As one of the best goose producers advises: 'Look to the colour of the skin. If it's golden, you know the bird must have been grass and corn fed. And that makes for a far tastier bird.'

G B Geese

Lings View Farm, 10 Middle Street, Croxton Kerrial, Grantham, Lincolnshire, NG32 1QP

Tel: 01476 870394 Fax: 01476 870394

Contact: Ann Botterill. Last orders: 1 December. No credit cards. Delivery charge: one bird, £13; two birds, £14; three birds, £15.

If you happen to be passing through the pretty village of Croxton Kerrial, you may well see Ann Botterill's geese gaggling around the various fields. She keeps them all over the place in smallish groups of about 300. That is, Ann believes, how they best thrive: grazing on grassland, feeding on own-grown wheat and oats, with plenty of water to drink but no ponds to swim in. 'Definitely not. We keep them off water, because if they start swimming it turns their meat tough.'

Killed on-farm at any age between 18 and 26 weeks, the geese are hung for ten days and sold oven ready weighing 4.5–6kg. The birds, complete with vacuum-packed giblets and a wodge of goose fat, come neatly trussed and dressed, and cost around £6 per kg.

Ann also prepares two versions of stuffed goose. The birds are boned, and stuffed either with diced chicken and pheasant, or pork and pheasant mixed with herbs and apricots. Working with a French chef who cooks nearby, she has also developed a truly authentic goose rillette. Made from goose legs and belly of pork, seasoned with various herbs, salt and pepper, the meats are simmered together until tender, then shredded by fork for just the right texture. For French-born food writer Marie-Pierre Moine, the pleasure of rillette lies 'in the sensation of soft, salty filaments of meat suspended in their fat that melt away in the mouth', whereas a more pragmatic Ann describes it as 'potted meat with texture'. Either way hers is a good example, and comes in a 240g jar or a 1.4kg dish, prices available on application.

Goodman's Geese

Walsgrove Farm, Great Witley, Worcester, Worcestershire, WR6 6JJ

Tel: 01299 896272 Fax: 01299 896889

Contact: Judy Goodman. Last orders: 20 November. No credit cards. Delivery charge: one bird, £11; two birds, £15; three birds, £17.

Judy Goodman grows 1,500 Kelly Bronze turkeys, but it is for her geese that she has built her reputation. Possibly the largest producer of free-range geese in Britain, this year she promises more than 3,000 for Christmas. Her geese waddle about in the fields, kept at a stocking density of around 100 birds per acre, and graze contentedly on the grass, supplemented with a compound feed of minerals, wheat and barley made up to her specifications. They are slaughtered by dislocation of the neck – the approved method – at any age between 22 and 28 weeks; dry-plucked; hung for 10 to 14 days; and sold oven ready at a weight range of 10–13lb.

Carefully hand plucked for an unbruised, unbroken flesh, Judy's birds come particularly well presented, trussed with string to make stuffing easier, the full complement of giblets, a chunk of goose fat and a bunch of fresh herbs. These are magnificent, meaty birds: comparatively lean, with a good bone-to-meat ratio and moist, deeply resonant flesh. Some geese may shrink during cooking, but not Judy's. Her secret lies in how she rears them, taking care they are 'never frightened or frustrated, well fed but not overly so. We never bring them on too fast; if we did they would turn to fat. And we only slaughter them when they are mature, so you get better textured and flavoured meat'.

A 12lb goose, which because it includes fat and giblets goes into the oven at 10lb, Judy reckons 'is ample for eight greedy eaters' - although I think that is erring on the generous side. I find 1lb per person adequate, particularly with her geese. They cost just under £3 a pound, but be warned: Judy's geese are in great demand and sell out, so book early.

Holly Tree Farm Shop

Chester Road, Tabley, Knutsford, Cheshire, WA16 0EU

Tel: 01565 651835 Fax: 01565 651835 email: bailey@hollytree.u-net.com

Contact: Karol Bailey. Last orders: 15 December. No credit cards. Delivery charge: £12.50 for up to 10kg.

Karol Bailey rears around 1,000 geese for Christmas. Kept out in the field, they feed on grass supplemented with a corn-based ration. Her birds are pale fleshed with a mild gamey flavour and a moist creamy texture. Hung for between seven and ten days, they are hand plucked, dipped in wax for a clean smooth finish, dressed with the livers, gizzard, heart, neck and a bag of goose fat stuffed inside the bird's cavity, and left unsewn to make stuffing easier. Available in a range of weights from 7 to 14lb, they cost £2.95 per pound.

Using her own geese, she prepares a Goose Banquet Roll from a whole boned goose rolled around layers of turkey breast and own-cured ham, or turkey breast and pheasant breast, filled with a choice of one of her stuffings (see page 66). A roll can weigh between 8 and 15lb, and costs £7 per pound. Karol reckons a pound in weight should easily feed two guests.

She also prepares a coarse goose terrine, using goose livers and goose meat flavoured with various spices and a generous splash of sherry. Sold in 4oz and 8oz pots sealed with a layer of clarified butter, they cost £4 and £8 respectively. Then there are her excellent chunky goose sausages, which come in a choice of spiced or lightly smoked. And, if you like the flavour of smoked goose, you should try her smoked goose breasts and legs. Karol brines these in a salt brine flavoured with dry sherry, ginger and soy sauce for about five days, and then sends them off to Mooreland Foods (see page 21) for smoking.

Seldom Seen Farm

Billesdon, Leicester, Leicestershire, LE7 9FA

Tel: 0116 259 6742 Fax: 0116 259 6626

Contact: Claire Symington. Last orders: 10 December. No credit cards.

Delivery charge: £8 per bird.

Every year Claire Symington rears even more geese; such is their ever increasing popularity. For this Christmas, she promises about 1,500 in total, of which about 600 will be boned out for her Three Bird Roast.

This amazing confection consists of a boned goose, stuffed with a boned chicken, stuffed with a boned pheasant. Between each bird Claire spreads a layer of own-made stuffing of minced pork meat (she is very particular to stress it is pork rather than sausage meat, as the latter would be rather fatty), wholemeal breadcrumbs, juice and grated orange rind, onions, celery, parsley and dried sage. Her Three Bird Roast is particularly popular as not only does it taste magnificent hot or cold, but it is also easy to carve and 'makes a goose go further'. Available fresh or frozen, a roast can weigh anything from 10 to 12lb which will feed 12 to 15 guests and cost £4.90 per pound.

The rest of her birds are sold fresh and oven ready, complete with giblets and a generous dollop of their butter-yellow fat. Because her geese free-range on grass and are fed on own-grown potatoes and corn, their flesh is a distinctive yellow with a deep meaty flavour. These birds are available in a range of weights from 8 to 15lb, costing £2.60 per pound, and Claire recommends allowing 1¼lb per person. For the greatest economy she also suggests carving the breast off in one piece, and then cutting it into slices across the grain.

Locals also know to visit the farm shop during December, when it is open between 9.30 and 5.30 all day up until Christmas Eve, seven days a week. The aim here is to provide everything for the meal, and as Clare was once head cook at Leith's Catering most of what is on sale will be own-made. Expect to find a whole range of cakes, puddings, mince pies, shortbread, jellies, jams, stuffings, brandy butter, 'treats' such as peppermint creams or nut brittle, and dishes like shepherd's pie for freezing over the holidays. From the farm come Christmas trees, holly wreaths, and Brussels sprouts on the stalks so that they remain fresh and firm for as long as possible.

Apple and Brandy Stuffing

For an easy stuffing for a goose, simply take three large Bramley apples. Wash, core and roughly chop, but do not peel them. (It is not necessary, and anyway the peel gives texture.) Add the juice and grated rind of a lemon, a couple of crushed cinnamon sticks, a generous handful of sultanas and 45ml (three generous tablespoons) of brandy. Cover and leave to soak in a cool place overnight. Just before you stuff the goose, chop its liver coarsely and add. (If you want to save it for a terrine, you can always substitute 100g (4oz) trimmed chicken livers.) Finally, stir in a handful of freshly chopped parsley or sage, and season generously. Spoon into the neck cavity.

Chicken

Haycorn's Farm

Mount Carmel Road, Palestine, Andover, Hampshire, SP11 7ES

Tel: 01264 889546 Fax: 01264 889546

email: haycornsfarm@andover.co.uk

Contact: David Stevens. Last orders: 10 December. No credit cards. Delivery charge: £13 for any order up to 10kg.

A few years ago I was sent a Briar Blue chicken to sample. It was superb, the sort of bird that dreams are made of, with its rich meatiness, firm but moist flesh and reverberating flavour.

Bred from the poulet de Bresse with a commercial broiler, the Briar Blue has all the flavour advantages of the French bird but, as David Stevens points out, 'with a filled-out shape'. The French may value their bird and be prepared to pay well over the odds for the pure sensation of its taste, but we British dismiss it as 'scrawny'. So a meatier and fuller-breasted Briar Blue seems the perfect compromise.

It was Sutherland's of Eldon, in their search for 'something different', who originally had the idea to crossbreed the bird, but now David is running with it. Flavour, he believes, is inherent in the breed, which is why he is keen to develop it. But his flocks are still small, and he expects to have fewer than 300 to 400 birds for Christmas. Kept in small groups of about 100, so they truly do have plenty of space to free range, for optimum flavour the birds are fed an additive-free corn-based ration, and reared for between 16 and 18 weeks, more than double the life of most birds you pick off a supermarket shelf.

Throughout the year, David's birds weigh between 3½ and 8lb, although at Christmas he takes cockerels on to 20 weeks to reach an impressive 10lb oven ready, costing £2.50 per pound. Hung for about a week, these are fine birds, 'something', as David says, 'to get your teeth into with the true old-fashioned chicken taste'.

Johnson & Swarbrick

Swainson House Farm, Goosnargh Lane, Goosnargh, Nr Preston, Lancashire, PR3 2JU

Tel: 01772 865251

Contact: Reg Johnson. Last orders: 1 November. No credit cards. Delivery charge: p&p extra.

Reg Johnson, unlike David Stevens of Haycorn's Farm (see above), does not believe that breed is important for a chicken's flavour. He says: 'it's how you rear and feed the bird that makes the difference', and buys in commercial chicks whose breed, he cheerfully admits, he does not even know.

But with such successful and demanding northern restaurants as Heathcote's (see page 185) and Mash and Air as his customers (as well as Le Gavroche in London), he must be doing it right. Fed an additive-free, corn-based ration 'to give them texture and flavour', the birds are reared semi-intensively for nine to ten weeks for a 3½lb bird and 14 to 18 weeks for capon size. 'And it's the extra age which gives them even more flavour and texture.'

Their usual weight is around the 3 to 5lb mark, but he will keep birds back taking them on to 8 to 9lb for the Christmas table. Please, though, do give Reg plenty of warning, as everything is grown to order.

Piper's Farm

Cullompton, Exeter, Devon, EX15 1SD

Tel: 01392 881380 Fax: 01392 881600

Contact: Peter Greig. Last orders: 18 December. Switch, MasterCard, Visa. Delivery charge: minimum order £40; £10 carriage charge.

Until I had tasted a chicken from Piper's Farm, I had always thought that breed of bird was important. But the extraordinary fact is that deeply flavoured, succulent and well-textured though their birds are, they are no more than a common or garden commercial hybrid breed. This only goes to prove that it is how the birds are reared, fed, slaughtered and hung that is important. Piper's Farm rear theirs in the 'traditional way' for 12 to 14 weeks, feeding them on a straight cereal-based diet, slaughtering them on-farm, and dry plucking and hanging them for 10 to 14 days. That having been said, they are experimenting with various cross-breeds and have introduced some old-fashioned British strains.

Meanwhile the bird you buy has a satisfying rich creaminess that reverberates on. Usually weighing around 5lb and costing £2.63 per pound, for Christmas they take them on up to 8lb. Buy it as a whole bird, or a whole boned bird at £5.88 per lb, or a gigot (boneless thigh) or boned breast costing £5.95, with a choice of apricots, hazelnuts and fresh herbs, or pesto and brown breadcrumb stuffings.

Duck

Holly Tree Farm Shop

Chester Road, Tabley, Knutsford, Cheshire, WA16 0EU
Tel: 01565 651835 Fax: 01565 651835 email: bailey@hollytree.u-net.com
Contact: Karol Bailey. Last orders: 15 December. No credit cards. Delivery charge: £12.50 for up to 10kg.

Apart from geese, Karol Bailey also rears pole-barn turkeys and free-range ducks. Outside all day, her ducks feed on grass supplemented with a corn ration, and take 16 to 20 weeks to reach their 4 to 8lb table weight.

Somewhat unusually, she favours the Pekin breed. 'They're a meaty, tasty little bird and I really like their flavour. I find the other breeds never make the size, and although they do have a tendency to put on too much fat I avoid that by regulating their diet. I just cut down on the corn.' Sold hung for seven to ten days, oven ready and complete with liver, a duck costs £2.35 per pound. To be on the safe side, you should allow 1lb per person.

Karol also prepares a Duck Banquet Roll on similar lines to the goose version (see page 35). She bones out a whole duck and rolls it around a choice of turkey breast and own-cured ham, or turkey breast and pheasant breast, and then fills it with a choice of her stuffings. It costs £5.85 per pound, but there is absolutely no wastage. They are remarkably easy to carve, and one pound of meat should adequately – if not generously – feed two guests.

Potato, Onion, Sage and Lemon Stuffing

This is a substantial yet light and plain stuffing, but with enough punch to stand up to the flavour of a goose or duck. This quantity is enough for a 2kg (4½lb) bird; for a larger one, either double the quantities or use different stuffings at each end.

700g (1½lb) potatoes
2 large onions
25g (1oz) rendered goose fact, duck fat or butter
1 garlic clove
15ml (1 tbsp) chopped fresh sage leaves
Grated rind of large lemon
Salt and freshly milled black pepper

Peel the potatoes and cut them into small chunks. Cook in salted water, drain and roughly mash. Meanwhile peel, halve and slice the onions. Fry them over a medium heat in the goose fact (or duck fat or butter) until soft and brown. Peel and chop the garlic. Mix together the potato, onion, garlic, sage and lemon rind. Season generously with salt and pepper. Season the cavity with salt, and spoon in the stuffing.

From *In Praise of the Potato* by Lindsey Bareham (Penguin)

Johnson & Swarbrick
Swainson House Farm, Goosnargh Lane, Goosnargh, Nr Preston, Lancashire, PR3 2JU
Tel: 01772 865251
Contact: Reg Johnson. Last orders: 1 November. No credit cards. Delivery charge: p&p extra.

Every duck producer has his or her favoured breed. Reg Johnson's is an Aylesbury–Pekin cross. His ducks have a good flavour – 'ducky' being the best description Reg could come up with – and, as a result of their short muscle fibre, 'an extra tender, melting texture'. They are reared on straw for 60 days, and fed a high protein, wheat-based ration. Reg also makes a point of 'feeding them away from fat', so expect a light covering of fat over the breast.

Dry plucked and hung for 24 to 48 hours, they weigh between 4 and 5½lb oven ready with giblets included, and cost £1.60 per pound.

Richard Waller

Long Grove Wood Farm, 234 Chartridge Lane, Chesham,
Buckinghamshire, HP5 2SG
Tel: 01494 772744 Fax: 01494 772744
Contact: Richard Waller. Last orders: 7 December. No credit cards. Personal shoppers only.

The Aylesbury duck has a chequered history. Once highly sought after, there were plenty of small scale 'duckers' in and around the town keeping them as a sideline, and every farm worker ran a small flock. Then they fell out of favour as they were thought too large for restaurants and too fatty or, worse still, with not enough meat for private customers.

'That was the fault of the breeders, the ones who bred them for show,' Richard Waller, now the only remaining commercial producer of the pure-bred Aylesbury duck, told me. 'Sure, they would get points for the shape of the beak and its colour, but you take the feathers off and there was damn all to put on the table.' The bloodline of Richard's ducks goes back to the 1770s, when the family first kept them, but his ducks with their well-covered breasts have obviously never been 'improved'.

An Aylesbury is easily recognisable by its white feathers, flattened shape and keel, and a beak 'as pink as a lady's thumbnail'. Once his ducklings are hardened off, they live outdoors, although they are shut in at night. Believe it or not, according to Richard they do not like the wet and go indoors to shelter from the rain. 'They'll swim on a pond all right, but they do not like the wet on their backs. It washes away their waterproofing.'

Richard tends a flock of about 2,000 ducks producing around 300 ducklings a week that are 'matched, hatched and dispatched with 12 weeks'. They are fed a specially formulated commercial feed ('with no drugs' Richard insists) but with additional wheat for a light-coloured flesh and a firmer fat, and a little barley. The ducks are slaughtered in the traditional way by wringing their necks, are dry plucked, waxed and hung uneviscerated for 48 hours. They weigh around 5 to 5½lb oven-ready, cost £1.40 per pound, and will feed four generously. For Christmas he takes some ducks on to almost nine weeks for a 6 to 7lb weight; 'but it's a fine balance, as this is the time they start putting on fat and growing feathers. And you just don't want them too fatty or with feathers poking through the skin. They look awful.'

If you've never had a true Aylesbury, you have a treat in store. They are well fleshed, with a thin layer of fine flavoured fat that is hard and solid, 'more like the consistency of beef than pork'. If it's soft, says Richard, 'it is not a true Aylesbury'. The meat is distinctly pale, almost the colour of pork, remarkably tender with virtually no grain, and has a pronounced gamey flavour. Fashion, Richard has noticed, has come full circle. He is delighted that restaurants are crying out for them again and that the number of his private customers grows weekly.

Hereford Duck Company

Trelough House, Wormbridge, Hereford, HR2 9DH

Tel: 01981 570767 Fax: 01981 5705779

Contact: Barry Clark. Last orders: 1 December. No credit cards. Delivery charge: £7.20 for orders under £50; £2.50 for orders £50-£100; carriage free for orders over £100.

Barry Clark has developed his own strain of duck – the Trelough – named after his house. Its main bloodline is the large Rouen duck from Normandy, mixed with various domestic ducks, and was bred by Barry for flavour, texture, comparative leanness, a good meat-to-bone ratio, generous breasts and a quick maturity.

This is the duck you will often eat at some of our trendiest restaurants (I think it was at Marco Pierre White's Quo Vadis that I last saw it on the menu) and indeed it is very good. The flavour, with its deep fruity resonance, is most pleasing and its texture pliable and compact.

A Trelough takes about 10 to 16 weeks to be ready for the table, when it weighs from 4 to 6½lb. Barry thinks the ideal weight is around 5lb. 'You get good sized breasts – about 8oz each side – and not too much fat. The danger, once the birds get heavier, is that they start to put on too much fat.' Sold oven ready, with the giblets wrapped up inside the bird, they cost £2.50 per pound, and you should allow 1lb per person. Barry also supplies ducks New York dressed (plucked but uneviscerated, and with head and legs on) at £2.10 per pound, packs of four breasts at £6.75 per pound, and packs of 4 legs at £2.95 per pound.

He also sells other things duck. Keen cooks may well be interested in the frozen carcasses at 60p per pound for making stock and soups; the 2lb packs of ducks' livers for terrines or pâtés at £4 per pound; and the jars of rendered duck fat that transform roast potatoes into the best treat imaginable. Then there are the juicy sausages made from breast and leg meat, shallots, various herbs and seasonings; and the confit. This comes in a jar of either two or six duck legs (at £6 or £14 respectively) that have been cured in rock salt and rosemary, baked in the oven until they are meltingly soft and then packed in the strained fat.

Game Birds and Peacock

Derek Fox
25 Market Place, Malton, Yorkshire, YO17 OLP
Tel: 01653 600338
Contact: Derek Fox. Last orders: 18 December. No credit cards. Delivery charge: £10.80 for up to 4kg.

If most of the year butcher Derek Fox just supplies meat and game, at Christmas-time he comes into his own with his Yorkshire Pots. Based on an old extravagant Yorkshire recipe of boned-out birds laid one within the other which started with peacock and finished with quail, his pots are made with duck, chicken, pheasant, partridge and venison wrapped around the birds' livers.

In between each bird is a layer of stuffing, three different ones and usually saffron, chestnut and chive. When you cut into the pot, the whole effect is 'like a jam Swiss roll'. 'We're going for colour and contrast here, the dark of the duck against the white of the chicken, the dark of the pheasant, the pale partridge and the deep red of the venison, with the coloured stuffings in between. And the livers to give even more flavour.'

The arduous work of boning-out starts with the pheasant season in October, but provided you give Derek notice he will make a pot out of more or less anything. His standard pot, the one I described, weighs about 7½lb, is guaranteed to feed ten to twelve people, and costs £32. All pots are sent frozen, so if you prefer to buy fresh you will have to call at the shop.

Fayre Game
Lodge Lane Nurseries, Lodge Lane, Lytham, Lancashire, FY8 5RP
Tel: 01253 738640 Fax: 01253 730002
Last orders: 19 December. No credit cards. Delivery charge: £9.99 for up to 15kg.

The owners of Fayre Game are quail farmers, and they will send quail and other fresh game (although strictly speaking the quail is not a game bird) to anywhere in the country. In season they have supplies of pheasant, partridge (both red- and grey-legged), grouse, mallard, widgeon, pigeon, venison, hare and rabbit.

They have also just launched an interesting range of boned and stuffed birds. To give them a pleasing plumped-up shape, the boning is done on traditional lines by boning-out the breast and wings, while leaving the drumsticks intact. Starting with the quail, this is exotically stuffed with Camargue red rice, minced pork, onions, dried apricots and raisins. Flavoured with a hint of orange, it makes for a nicely textured combination that perks up what can be a relatively bland bird. Each quail weighs around 100g, enough for one, and a two-bird pack costs between £3.20 and £3.50.

A single maize-fed guinea fowl, stuffed with apple, pork, onion and apricots, costs £5.95 and should feed three to four. Also for three to four and costing £4.99 is a pleasingly gamey boned and stuffed pheasant. Its stuffing is rather more robust, made with chicken livers, pork, walnuts and apricots. And promised for late autumn, in time for Christmas, is a pistachio and raisin stuffed partridge.

Needing no preparation whatsoever and only a simple roasting in the oven (exact times are printed on the packs), these birds are bound to solve several problems over the holidays

Glebedale Peacocks

Parsonage Farm, Llandewi Skirrid, Abergavenny, Monmouthshire, NP7 8AG

Tel: 01873 854358 Fax: 01873 853942

Contact: Jill Williams. Last orders: 1 November. No credit cards. Personal shoppers only.

Should you be extravagant enough to want a peacock for Christmas, either as decoration or to eat, this is the place to go. Jill Williams has always kept peacocks, and has a few to sell for the table. Eating them, she thinks, is not much fun as the birds do not carry a lot of flesh at the best of times. To counteract this, Jill keeps them in a barn so they cannot fly about, and feeds them up. Even so, the breast is quite dry and the thighs quite gamey. On the other hand, a peacock looks tremendous as a centrepiece, particularly if you have the male's tail fanned out to reveal all its sumptuousness. Apparently one customer went to the lengths of skinning the bird, cooking it wrapped up in foil, then presenting it at table with its skin and feathers laid back on top. It was some centrepiece.

Jill can sell them dressed and oven ready, but for obvious reasons most people buy them still in feather. A cock bird costs £75 and a hen – although no-one wants one as its feathers are so dowdy – costs £40.00. All I can add to that is: good luck. If you do buy one, please let me know how you get on.

If you cannot find one near you, some game merchants are prepared to supply by overnight delivery. Species, prices and condition of game birds and venison (see also page 54) vary, but highly recommended are the following:

Macbeth's, 11 Tolbooth Street, Forres, Moray Grampian, IV36 0DB (Tel and fax: 01309 672254)

Round Green Venison Company, Round Green Farm, Worsborough, Barnsley, Yorkshire, S75 3DR (Tel: 01226 205577, Fax: 01226 281294)

Teesdale Trencherman, Startforth Hall, Barnard Castle, Co Durham, DL12 9RA (Tel: 01833 638370)
Welsh Venison Centre, Middlewood Farm, Bwlch, Powys, LD3 7HQ (Tel: 01874 730929)
The Game Larder, 562 Chessington Road, Ewell, Epsom, Surrey, KT19 9HJ (Tel: 0181 391 9000)

Beef

Donald Russell Direct

Harlaw Road, Inverurie, Aberdeenshire, AB51 4FR
Tel: 01467 629666 Fax: 01467 624200
Contact: Joyce Kindness. Last orers: 17 December. No credit cards. Delivery charge: £9 for orders under £100.

Beef remains a controversial issue. Some resolutely refuse to eat it, others act as if no warnings have ever been issued. But sensible food lovers choose their sources carefully, opting for grass-fed cattle from declared BSE-free herds.

Donald Russell had a successful company supplying beef, with 98 per cent of its meat sold abroad to hotels and restaurants. Needless to say, it was badly hit by the recent beef export ban, but necessity being the mother of invention. then focused on developing a British market. Their loss has proved our gain, as Donald Russell Direct now supplies straight to the home.

Based in Aberdeenshire, Donald Russell understandably deals in Scottish meat, buying in from local farms. Beef, described as from 'Aberdeen Angus-type cattle', is actually from Aberdeen Angus crossed with Limousin or Charolais, the large Continental breeds. I was told that this cross giveswhat is wanted: a bigger carcass for bigger cuts and good marbling. Only grass-fed steer beef, 'free from additives, hormones and recycled protein', is sold, with each beast 'trace[able] back to farm of origin'. They are slaughtered at 16 to 22 months, and if you think that sounds a little young, apparently cross breeds mature earlier than traditional breeds.

All the meat is hung for up to three weeks on the bone in the traditional manner, butchered and vacuum packed. It is, I am assured, always fresh and never frozen, but arrives vacuum-packed to extend its shelf-life for 15 days. I followed the instructions to the letter, opened a pack of steaks on the 15th day exactly and they were good: succulent, finely grained if perhaps a little soft in texture (this may be a result of the vacuum-packing). Perhaps the meat should be allowed to drain and sit a while in the open air, as I cannot imagine it does much for it all scrunched up in plastic. The only off-putting factor was the strong smell that is delicately referred to as a 'slight odour' when you first cut open the pack. You are warned.

Butchering is of the highest standard, with some interesting cuts not always seen in the butchers' shops. There are thick cut and excessively well trimmed pavé rump steaks or *tafelspitz* (rump caps) and rib eye roll (boned); and for the main meal a five-bone rib. With an average weight of 4.5kg, this looks impressive when served, has a fine-grained texture and a relatively resonant flavour, and costs £8.50 a kilo.

Macbeth's

20 Tolbooth Street, Forres, Moray, IV36 0PH

Tel: 01309 672254 Fax: 01309 672254

Contact: Susan Gibson. Last orders: 15 December. Visa. Delivery charge: £12.50 for orders up to £250; thereafter carriage free.

Beef sold at Macbeth's is from Michael Gibson's own herd, or bought in from local farms, or from the Orkneys. Here you will find meat only from 100 per cent beef breeds – pure-bred Aberdeen Angus, pure-bred Beef Shorthorn, pure-bred Highland Cattle and Aberdeen Angus–Shorthorn cross – with not, you will notice, a drop of foreign blood between them. The introduction of continental breeds such as Limousin and Charolais, he believes, has done our beef no favours. They may have increased the size but they have diluted the flavour.

In summer the cattle are fed on grass; in winteron hay, sugar-beet pulp, silage and distillery by-products: a sort of corn mash. In the Highlands it is quite usual for cattle to be fed on this, and I can assure you it does not mean they taste of whisky. Michael's strengths lie in how he finishes his beef cattle. 'They have to be slaughtered at the right weight for butchering, and at the right maturity for eating.' Finishing an animal is a skilled business. To get the right flavour, says Michael, you have to get the right degree of marbling through the meat. 'Marbling is a function of maturity. Until an animal reaches a certain age, it won't lay any significant marbling down unless you are grossly overfeeding it. And if you have pushed it, the meat will be lighter in colour. It may be tender, but it will be bland like processed cardboard. But a properly reared animal will have close-textured, firm meat with a fine marbling for flavour.'

All the beef is hung for 17 days, and is cut to order by his staff, or 'technicians' as he likes to call them. 'We butcher every which way, in traditional cuts or continental seaming, and we'll send whatever you want. If you just want a fillet, we'll send you a fillet.' As for which of the breeds you should choose, in fact most of his customers do not specify; but if you want to Michael will be delighted to accommodate you provided you are prepared to wait if necessary. The differences are minimal, but when pushed he describes Highland as bigger with more flavour, Aberdeen Angus as richer and slightly fattier 'with not quite the edge', and Shorthorn as somewhere between the two.

For Christmas, Michael's wife, Susan, who runs the shop, recommends a 10lb sirloin on the bone, enough to feed 15. This size of joint cooks better than smaller ones, and is normally around £6 per pound. It is a real luxury and, says Susan, beats a rib joint hands down. And at a recent lunch I had with chef Beth Coventry, she pronounced it 'rough and ready – coarse grained but a truly wonderful flavour'.

Piper's Farm

Cullompton, Exeter, Devon, EX15 1SD

Tel: 01392 881380 Fax: 01392 881600

Contact: Peter Greig. Last orders: 18 December. Switch, MasterCard, Visa.

Delivery charge: minimum order £40, £10 carriage charge.

Peter Greig of Piper's Farm favours traditional breeds, so it is fitting that his beef is from pure-bred North Devons (Ruby Reds), native to the area. Single-suckled until six months, reared on Exmoor then brought down to be finished at Piper's Farm, where they have a clover-rich permanent pasture, they are slaughtered at around 30 months. Ruby Red beef is often overlooked in the rush for the better known Aberdeen Angus or Hereford; but when properly reared and hung (Peter hangs his for at least four weeks), it is excellent. With its rich veins of intra-muscular fat and fine-textured grain, it has a glorious succulence and a full-bodied punch. It is butchered into various cuts, in both the British and Continental styles. Peter recommends a joint of topside at £4.85 per pound or £10.67 per kilo, or rolled sirloin at £7.94 per pound or £17.45 per kilo.

Lamb comes as a Suffolk North of England mule cross, because he believes it has a good meat-to-bone ratio. Slaughtered at between eight and fourteen months for a lingering grassiness, it too comes in various cuts. If a plain roasted leg or shoulder is not quite special enough for the meal, you could try one of Piper's Farm's boned and stuffed joints. There is a choice of apricot, hazelnut and peach; plain pesto; coriander and garlic; and rosemary and garlic stuffings; with a boned and stuffed shoulder costing £5.34 per pound or £11.77 per kilo with a weight range of 1 to 2 kilos. A similarly prepared leg costs £6.90 per pound or £15.18 per kilo, with a weight range of between 500g and 2kg.

Lamb

Agnus Quality Meats

Low Wool Oaks, Calthwaite, Penrith, Cumbria, CA11 9RZ
Tel: 01768 885384 Fax: 01768 885384
Contact: C Anthony Head. Last orders: 12 December. No credit cards. Delivery charge: £9.50.

The Herdwick, the indigenous breed of sheep in the Cumbrian Mountains, is thought to be the hardiest breed in Britain. Living in those climatic conditions, I would have thought it needs to be. One of its earliest mentions was in 1789, when James Clarke wrote in his *Survey of the Lakes*: 'There is a kind of sheep in these mountains called Herdwick ... they, contrary to all other sheep I have met with, are seen before a storm, especially of snow, to ascend against the coming blast, and take the stormy side of the mountain, which, fortunately for themselves, saves them from being overblown.'

Bred originally for their wool, their colour changes as the sheep mature. A new season's lamb's coat is dark brown and turns grey after its first shear; that, in turn, lightens the older it grows. 'D'ye ken John Peel, with his coat so grey' refers to his hunting coat, spun and woven from Herdwick wool.

Recently there has been a revival in eating Herdwick lamb either smoked (see the Old Smokehouse, page 22) or as fresh meat. I think this is altogether a good thing: it is about time we woke up to the possibility of regional and/or specific breeds, with their marked flavours and textures; and the Herdwick does have a distinct taste.

Herdwicks, as sold by Agnus Quality Meats, are all pure bred from registered breeders and come primarily from Borrowdale, Langdale, Wasdale and Eskdale. They graze in the fells on ling heather and blaeberries, and are brought down to the lowlands to be finished on grass. Up there, the sheep lamb late, not until April to May, so the new season's lamb with its carcass weight of around 32lb is not ready for the table until October, with a season lasting through to May.

In the area, the best lamb is thought to be the 'shearling', meaning when it has had its first shear or is 12 months old. This is when the meat has its sweeter, more distinctive flavour and has acquired its rich vein of marbling. Understandably Mr Head is reluctant to stress this, as he believes (rightly) that anyone outside of the Lakes will turn up their nose at what is technically mutton. Although you can buy new season lamb and it is good, trust me and go for the shearling. Finely grained, it has a deeper, richer and stronger flavour while still being surprisingly lean and juicy. A leg or loin weighing 4 to 5lb should be hung for at least a week You can, if you wish, also order mutton: proper mutton over three years old, with all the strength of flavour that implies. All their Herdwick meat is hung for ten days, and comes as whole or half carcasses or in various joints or cuts.

Chesterton Farm Shop

Chesterton Lane, Cirencester, Gloucestershire, GL7 6JP

Tel: 01285 642160 Fax: 01285 653133

Contact: Gary Wallace. Last orders: 28 November. Delivery charge: next day delivery before 10 am, £20.27; before 1 pm, £13.22.

Gary Wallace of the Chesterton Farm Shop was the first butcher nominated by the Rare Breed Survival Trust under its Traditional Meat Foundation scheme. It licences butchers to sell meat from pure-bred rare breeds, thus ensuring that these breeds have a more useful purpose than just a tourist attraction in visitor farms.

Many people, including such top chefs as Pierre Koffmann of Tante Claire and Martin Lam of Ransome's Dock, believe there is an inherent difference in eating qualities between rare and 'improved' modern breeds. The meat has a distinctive flavour, due to the distribution of the intra-muscular fat, and the carcasses have a different conformation (shape). The animals also develop more slowly (a reason why they became rare in the first place), and therefore tend to be slaughtered at a greater age. Thus muscle flavour has longer to develop.

For his Christmas dinner Gary is, as you might expect, going for rare-breed lamb. 'I'm biased in favour of the primitive breeds: the Shetland, Hebridean or Manx Loughton. These are the real unimproved breeds, and you can't beat them for flavour. At this time of year they are at their best. In spring, the new-born lambs are not really worth the eating as they're too small, too lean and have too low a bone-to-meat ratio. There's hardly any flesh. They're very slow maturers and have to be allowed to mature in their own time. From late autumn until May, they eat magnificently.' He recommends a leg or shoulder, with the joints coming relatively small. A leg weighs 3 to 3½lb, a shoulder around 4lb; but as the lambs are small boned, it means more meat than usual. They cost, depending on the breed, £20 to £25 and £15 to £20 respectively.

'Primitive lamb,' Gary warns, 'takes some cooking. Technically these are hoggets (over-wintered lambs), so if you were to roast them they won't be that tender. Far better to wrap the joint in foil with some herbs and garlic, and steam roast it for about 20 minutes to the pound. Then leave it unwrapped for the last 10 minutes to crispen the skin.' According to Gary, you will not be disappointed.

Lingcombe Farm Produce
Lingcombe Farm, Chagford, Newton Abbot, Devon, TQ13 8EF
Tel: 01647 433300
Contact: Stuart Baker. Last orders: 30 November. No credit cards. Delivery charge: £11 for up to 10kg.

Stuart Baker has worked with sheep for over 40 years and there is probably very little he does not know about them. He tends two flocks on his farm right up against the Common: local speak for Dartmoor. Even though he does have extensive grazing rights up on Dartmoor, he does not keep his lambs there because 'the grass is just not good enough to produce the quality I want'. Quality is certainly Stuart's watchword, and his lamb is so fine that the prestigious Gidleigh Park Hotel would not even consider serving anyone else's.

This Christmas he will have his Charolais-cross Dartmoor ready for the table. Michael Caine, Gidleigh Park's chef, reckons this is the finest of breeds and pronounces its meat 'the real McCoy'. Hung for between seven and ten days, it is finely grained with a rich, grassy-sweet flavour. Sold as haunch (leg with chump attached), it weighs around 6 to 7lb and costs £2.50 per pound.

Stuart also sells mutton, mostly from the White-faced Dartmoor. What you and I think of as mutton – that is to say, a two- or three-year-old sheep – is but a pale imitation as far Stuart is concerned. 'Mutton to me is when it's got to the far end of its life. It has fulfilled its use: lost its teeth or can't lamb any longer. Then it's proper mutton. Anything from six to ten years old. And it must be hung for at least 14 days; sometimes it can go up to a month.' His mutton is excellent: tender, finely grained, not too fat, with a deep lingering taste that is certainly different from lamb and without a hint of the rankness that you usually associate with mutton. As Stuart says, 'Good mutton only comes from a ewe. I'd never sell anyone a ram.' Also sold as haunches, they weigh around 7lb and cost £1.90 per pound. But remember: never, ever, let mutton see a grill or a frying pan. 'The only way to cook mutton is to stew or roast it in the oven.' And after all those years of dealing with sheep, he must certainly know what he is talking about.

Gary Wallace of Chesterton Farm (see page 49) is one accredited rare-breed meat butcher. Others are:

F Simpson & Son, The Croft, Cockfield, Bishop Auckland, Co Durham, DL13 5AA (Tel: 01388 718264)
David Lishman, 25 Leeds Road, Ilkley, Leeds, LS29 8DP (Tel: 01943 609436)
Bursea Farm Shop, Holme Upon Spalding Moor, York, YO4 7DB (Tel: 01430 860348)
F C Phipps, Osborne House, Mareham-Le-Fen, Boston, Lincolnshire,

PE22 7RW (Tel: 01507 568235)
Berkswell Traditional Farmstead Meats, Larges Farm, Back Lane, Meriden, Warwickshire, CV8 7LD (Tel: 01676 522409)
Chatsworth Farm Shop, Stud Farm, Pilsley, Bakewell, Derbyshire, DE45 1UF (Tel: 01246 583392)
The Cotswold Gourmet, PO Box 26, Cirencester, Gloucestershir,e GL7 5TJ (Tel: 011285 860229)
Eastwood of Berkhamsted, 15 Gravel Path, Berkhamsted, Hertfordshire, HP4 2EF (Tel: 01442 865012)
John Brown Butchers, 73 Rances Lane, Wokingham, Berkshire, RG11 2LG (Tel: 01734 786258)
The Butcher's Shop, The Chalk, Iwerne Minster, Blandford, Dorset, DT11 8NA (Tel: 01747 811229)
P. Warren and Son, 1 Westgate Street, Launceston, Cornwall, PL15 9QT (Tel: 01566 772089)

Pork

Heal Farm Meats

Kings Nympton, Umberleigh, Devon, EX37 9TB
Tel: 01769 574341 Fax: 01769 572839
Contact: Anne Petch. Last orders: 9 December. Switch, Delta, MasterCard, Visa. Delivery charge: £8.50 for any order.

Heal Farm is a breeding centre approved by the Rare Breed Survival Trust, and here Anne Petch rears her rare breed pigs according to her own principles, 'based on humane animal husbandry, a common sense approach to medications and an abhorrence of the chemicals and methods used in modern food production'. There is, she believes, a difference in the eating qualities of rare and modern 'improved' breeds, due to the conformation of their carcasses and the distribution of the inter-muscular fat. Rare breed pigs are slower developers, and Anne slaughters them at the greater age of between five and six months, 'so it follows that their flavour must be more developed'.

Although Anne does sell north Devon 'Ruby Red' beef, and conventional and rare-breed lamb, rare-breed pigs are her first love and it is for her pork that she is best known. It is not surprising, therefore, that as an alternative to the ubiquitous bird she suggests a joint of pork. Her favourite is a loin or chine, saw-cut under the ribs and loosened behind the back bone. This way you have the choice of carving it into thick slices between the ribs or, if you prefer thinner slices, easing the ribs out first.

Cooking it is remarkably simple, and as the meat is well marbled with fat Anne claims it will be temptingly moist. An hour before cooking, she rubs the skin all over with salt for a 'bubbling crackling', then leaves it to stand. Just before it goes into the oven, she wipes it to get rid of any moisture and scatters over more salt. As she belongs to the 'fast and furious' school of cooking, she puts it into a fairly high oven, around 200°C/400°F/gas mark 6, and roasts it for 20 to 30 minutes per pound. The result is a fine piece of pork with good, dense old-fashioned crisp crackling, and an earthy, well-textured meat. A bone-in loin costs £8.51 per kg, and you should probably allow 300 to 450g per guest, particularly if you want some cold leftovers to serve over the holidays.

Pugh's Piglets

Bowgreave House Farm, Bowgreave, Garstang, Lancashire, PR3 1YE

Tel: 01995 602571 Fax: 01995 600126

Contact: Barry Pugh. Last order: 18 December. No credit cards. Delivery charge: £11 for up to 10kg.

You should be warned that a Pugh's suckling pig arrives with its head on. The squeamish may find this a little hard to take, but it makes a spectacular alternative to a bird for the Christmas meal.

A young piglet still milking (suckling) the mother is how most butchers define a suckling pig. *Larousse Gastronomique* suggests that it can be as old as two months and weigh as much as 15kg. On the other hand, Barry Pugh has his sent to slaughter from three weeks (when they weigh 8 to 10lb) up to 4½ weeks (when they can be as heavy as 17lb). What matters, in his view, is that they fit into a domestic cooker. A conventional oven takes a piglet up to 10 or 12lb, and an Aga fits a 16lb one which costs £50. If you allow 1lb per person, you can feed a fair number of guests.

Although Barry does not farm himself, he insists that the pigs he buys have an additive-free diet. 'Obviously they get no drugs as, apart from anything else, the withdrawal period is not long enough for a suckling pig.' Apparently at ten days the piglets 'start drinking and sniffing around for bits and pieces, are fed milk pellets, but of course are not weaned'. Suckling pig is handled differently from pork. Once slaughtered, it is immediately scalded and scraped to remove its hairs and the fine top layer of its skin. 'It is sent off quickly. You can't hang a suckling pig. Its flesh is so milky that if you do it turns slippy or greasy.'

They are delivered oven ready, cleaned and paunched (gutted) ready for stuffing, and complete with head and tail. Barry suggests roasting them in the oven as the most practical way of cooking, allowing approximately 20 minutes per pound. The meat of a suckling pig is softer textured, more delicately flavoured than pork, with a gentle milkiness.

You can also order a *porchetta*, an Italian speciality. The suckling pig is boned, then stuffed with fresh herbs (bay leaves, rosemary), garlic and seasonings. The shoulders and legs are cut off, boned and then rolled up with the boned carcass to make what Barry describes as 'a barrel', tied up at regular intervals with string. These come either whole with head on weighing between 8 and 14lb and costing around £58 to £60, or cut in quarters, individually rolled and strung. But as these are not sold individually, you still have to buy the whole animal.

Wild Boar

Barrow Boar

Fosters Farm, South Barrow, Yeovil, Somerset, BA22 7LN

Tel: 01963 440315 Fax: 01963 440901

Contact: Christina Baskerville. Last orders: 15 December. Switch, MasterCard, Visa. Delivery charge: £8.50 for any order.

Wild wild boar still roam the fields, forests and scrublands of France, northern Italy, Poland, Germany and Austria, but in Britain they became extinct in the 17th century. What we do have, however, is farmed wild boar. If you think it sounds like a contradiction in terms, I had better explain that wild boar is an actual species: *Sus scropha*. How you keep them makes not a jot of difference to their name, but it does affect their eating qualities.

Nigel Dauncey's pure-bred herd – or troop or sounder as he would have it – roam in fields in conditions that approximate the wild, with a stocking density that varies from one to five sows per acre. Each field is securely fenced, furnished with bales of straw for nesting, water holes for wallowing and trees for sheltering. They rummage for food, but unlike pigs do not dig up the ground. Their diet is supplemented with various root crops – stock-feed potatoes, beetroot, sugar beet, fodder beet etc. – and they will strip the berries around the fields. 'A natural diet for a good flavour,' is what Nigel prescribes, and for a firm-textured meat, 'as much exercise as possible'.

Although wild wild boar is thought by the French to be best eaten as *marcassin* (up to six months), Nigel does not slaughter his until at least 14 months. 'The wild-living wild boar have a much more varied diet, so they will be tastier when younger,' he explains. 'Ours do not develop a full-flavoured meat until later. At six months, frankly you wouldn't notice a marked difference between their meat and pork.' Nigel's wild boar are always bled after slaughter; so although their flesh is a darker, richer red than pork, it is not as deeply coloured as you might expect. His boar is hung for a minimum of 14 days; the older the beast the longer he will leave it to relax the fibre. As for the taste, it does have a deeper, more resonant flavour than pork – gamier, more rounded and gutsier – but it is pleasingly subtle, not at all intrusive or musty. It is also in the texture that you notice a difference. Boar meat has a much closer, longer grain, actually rather like beef, and it is surprisingly lean.

With an on-farm butchery, all the usual cuts and joints are available, including eye of loin steak, shoulder, or saddle, either on the bone or boned and rolled, with haunch as last year's Christmas favourite. A good roasting joint, a whole haunch (leg plus chump) costs £10.90 per kilo, and can weigh up to 5kg. Allowing 400g per person, this will feed 12 people. But they will butcher to your requirements, even joints as small as 1kg. Remember, though, that wild boar is sold skinned, so if you are expecting crackling you are in for a disappointment.

Nigel can also supply a whole baby wild boar. These weigh around 15lb, so you need a relatively large oven to fit one. They come head on, and like suckling pig are mild and buttery and not especially meaty. If you arc looking for something even more way out for the main course, try the bison reared in Wiltshire, ostrich, alligator, crocodile or even emu.

Venison

Fletchers of Auchtermuchty

Reediehill Deer Farm, Auchtermuchty, Fife, KY14 7HS

Tel: 01337 828369 Fax: 01337 827001

Contact: Nichola Fletcher. Last orders: 1 December. MasterCard, Visa.

Delivery charge: £9.95 standard, with smaller items sent by first-class post if cheaper; orders over £90 carriage free.

Fletchers is a founder member of the quality assurance scheme British Prime Venison, run by the British Deer Farmers' Association. If you buy venison with the BPV mark it is guaranteed to come from farmed deer less than 27 months old; that is fed on natural feedstuffs with no growth promoters; and is slaughtered, hung and butchered in approved premises. As far as Nichola Fletcher is concerned, the advantages of farmed over wild venison are reliability and consistency. 'It's not variable. As it's under 27 months, you know for certain the meat is going to be tender, as opposed to wild venison which can be any age. Also our deer are clean shot (we take a rifle to them in the field), so there's no stress. And we all know just how much stress can affect the texture of meat. Farmed deer are better fed and sheltered. We even house them in winter because of our ghastly weather; they can go out but they never do. It's infinitely preferable to the lot of the wild deer, that can starve or die of exposure when the weather gets rough.'

But what about taste? This is a tricky one, because we all probably want to believe that a wild deer, roaming with all of nature's glorious bounty to feed on, will have a better flavour. Nichola is quick to dispel that illusion. 'There are many things that affect taste and texture: age, how and where it's shot, and for how long it's been hung. Strangely, its diet doesn't affect the flavour of the meat. This is because in ruminants with many stomachs – such as a deer – flavour only goes into fatty tissue, and venison is almost completely fat free.'

Nichola farms red deer. All her meat is hung for between two and three weeks as a carcass, a point she particularly stresses as she is critical of dealers who hang their meat jointed and vacuum-packed so that it gains no flavour. For the Christmas meal, she serves saddle of venison on the bone to include both the sirloin and fillet – 'the best muscles' – that costs £8.30 per pound. Failing that, a haunch (leg), either on or off the bone, should do you proud. Prices range from £5.90 to £7.32 per pound. As for cooking it, Nicola is also quick to dispel the rumours that it is tricky. The secret, apparently, is to baste it during cooking and to let it rest before serving. She sends out precise instructions with her joints.

Roast Venison with Parsley and Onion Gravy

Serves 6–8

There are two secrets to roasting venison successfully so that it does not dry out. First you must marinade the joint to make it succulent, then you must start roasting it at a high temperature. This searing process seals in the juices and keeps it extra moist. I prefer my venison quite pink, but you prefer it well done you can increase the cooking time. But remember that it is a fine balance: if you do cook it too long, it may dry out. Venison, in particular, is one meat that really does benefit from resting once it has been cooked, so allow plenty of time.

1.75kg (4lb) haunch of venison

Marinade

25g (1oz) black peppercorns
12 juniper berries
6–8 cloves garlic, peeled
75ml (5 tbsp) olive oil
30ml (2 tbsp) red wine
Sprig of thyme
Sprig of rosemary
1 bay leaf

Sauce

150ml (¼pt) red wine
2 medium red onions, finely chopped
2 anchovy fillets, chopped
1 large bunch flat-leaf parsley
30ml (2 tbsp) extra-virgin olive oil
Sea salt and freshly ground black pepper
Dash of lemon juice (optional)

Trim the venison if necessary, and using a sharp knife make about five or six deep incisions all over the joint, straight into the meat itself, piercing the skin and down through into the meat.

To make the marinade, crush the black peppercorns, juniper berries and garlic cloves together in a mortar with a pestle to make a relatively smooth paste. Poke a little of this paste right down into the incisions and spread the remainder all over the venison to form a crust. Put the joint in a glass or stainless steel bowl. In a separate bowl mix the olive oil and red wine together, pour it over the venison and add the thyme, rosemary and bay leaf. Leave in a cool place to marinade for about 24 hours, turning the meat occasionally so it remains moist and gets plenty of opportunity to soak up the flavours of the marinade.

The following day, preheat the oven to 220°C/425°F/gas mark 7. Lift the venison carefully out of the bowl, lay it on a suitable roasting tray and spoon over the marinade from the bowl. Roast for about 20 minutes, then turn the oven down to 190°C/375°F/gas mark 5 and roast for a further ten minutes per 450g (1lb), basting it occasionally. Thus, for a 1.75kg (4lb) joint you will need one hour cooking time in total, including the initial time at the higher heat. Remove from the oven and rest for about 15 minutes in the roasting tray before serving. Once it is rested, lift the venison out of the roasting tray, place on a warmed serving dish and keep warm.

To make the sauce, place the roasting tray over a medium heat, add the red wine and, using a wooden spoon, stir and scrape to loosen any bits stuck to the bottom. At this point sieve the juices to get rid of the burnt bits (if any have stuck to the pan, it may be a good idea to give it a clean), then return the juices to the pan. Turn up the heat slightly, add the chopped onions and cook for a couple of minutes to soften while the liquid reduces by about one-third. Then stir in the anchovies, parsley and olive oil. Warm gently, adjust the seasoning, and add the lemon juice to sharpen the flavours if you think it is necessary.

Carve the venison into thin slices and serve with the sauce.

Butcher Shops

Some food lovers may prefer to buy direct from a butcher's shop. Recommended below are a few favourites with a reputation for quality, who can be relied on for well-sourced and well-hung meat and poultry.

Edwards of Conwy, 18 High Street, Conwy, LL32 8DE (Tel: 01492 592443) sells beef from two-year-old Welsh Black heifers hung for up to three weeks. Currently they are 'experimenting' selling local salt-marsh lamb. This is a delicacy in Brittany, where it has a reputation for its buttery texture and deeply flavoured meat. If it tastes as good over here, I can see no reason why it should not catch on.

Hepburns of Mountnessing, 269 Roman Road, Mountnessing, Brentwood, Essex, CM15 0UH (Tel: 01277 353289, Fax: 01277 355589) sells organic (to Soil Association standards) Highgrove lamb and beef, reared on HRH Prince Charles' estate in Gloucestershire. They cure hams, an excellent brine-cured bacon finished in maple syrup, tongue and silverside. Apart from own-made sweet and savoury pies, pâtés, brawn, and ready cooked dishes, they also make Dundee cake for Christmas and can be relied on as a good source of fresh beef suet for your Christmas pudding.

Murray Mitchell, 110 Market Street, St Andrews, KY16 9PB (Tel: 01334 474465)
With a window filled with a glorious display of Aberdeen Angus carcasses and trays of haggis, mealie and black puddings, Murray Mitchell has a good reputation for the quality of its meat. It also sells all sorts of useful 'bits and pieces' including ham houghs and lambs' sweetbreads.

C Lidgate, 110 Holland Park Avenue, London W11 4UA (Tel: 0171 727 8243, Fax: 0171 229 7160) is my local butcher – and very lucky I am too. It is run by David Lidgate, whose attitude is that quality is a chain where every factor from breed, feed, welfare, age of the beast and finish to the method of slaughter, temperature control, hanging, and the art of butchering must be taken into account. Service is first rate and nothing is too much trouble. If you want a piece of meat specially butchered, boned or rolled, 'it's all part of the service'. Even my dog Violet's marrow bone is chopped to a manageable size. Particularly worth a mention are the pies, made every day with fresh vegetables, own-made butter-based pastry and good cuts of meat. These are proper old-fashioned pies, with plenty of flavour and thick flour-based sauces.

D J Rolfe, Hatchmere House, Walsham-le-Willows, Suffolk. IP31 3BD (Tel: 01359 259225) attracts customers from miles around his small village butcher's shop. The staff bone and stuff all manner of things, including saddle of lamb with a stuffing of seasoned minced lamb with apricots and almonds; turkeys, chickens, ducks and geese; and they also prepare to order ballotines of boned birds with one stuffed within the other. Look out for the Suffolk-cure ham, the bacon brined in ale and molasses, and the dry-cured silverside of beef finished with a rub of mustard and spices.

The Butcher's Shop, Iwerne Minster, Nr Blandford, Dorset, DT11 8NA (Tel: 01747 811229) is tucked on to the end of a row of cottages, and has the thickest oak door imaginable. Beef, normally Hereford, is bought off local farms, and hung for a minimum of 14 days. For the best possible flavour they favour heifers. At Christmas there are local organically reared (to Soil Association Standards) geese, Bronze and Norfolk black turkeys and Mark Chilcott's 'heavy chickens' that can weigh up to 12 pounds. With a brine 'on the go', they usually have pickled brisket and tongue, and you can rely on finding 'bits and pieces' such as trotters and caul fat.

At Home

40 High Street, Cobham, Surrey, KT11 3EB

Tel: 01932 862026 Fax: 01932 867617

Contact: Marilyn Newman. Last orders: 21 December. MasterCard, Visa.

Delivery: free within a 50-mile radius for an order for ten people or more.

Short of taking the entire family out to lunch for a slap-up meal in a restaurant or hotel, I cannot think how you can better the deal offered by At Home. On Christmas Eve they will deliver a huge box that contains the entire meal ready prepared and ready to cook. This has got to be the answer to the ultimate non-cook's prayer.

Everything is made in the At Home kitchens, and arrives fresh and as good as (in some cases probably a lot better) than own-cooked. The 'prize-winning hen turkey' is wrapped in foil and arranged in a roasting tin. It has been stuffed at both ends and the breast is buttered and covered with lardons. All that's left for you to do is to slide it into the oven; and you will not even have to clean the tin afterwards as they do not want it back. Even the potatoes are peeled and soaking in water so they will not turn black.

The menu for this year's feast sounds tempting enough. As a starter there is terrine of fresh lobster, crab and prawn wrapped in smoked salmon, served with a tiny cucumber salad with a separate dill and sour-cream dressing. The main course is turkey with two stuffings – minced pork and chestnuts, lemon thyme and breadcrumbs or cracked wheat, pinenuts and apricots – a 'proper' turkey gravy, 'proper' bread sauce, own-made cranberry sauce with port, chipolatas wrapped in bacon, potatoes with goose fat to roast them in, Brussels sprouts with chestnuts and a winter root vegetable purée. Then there is the pudding, plus mince pies with Armagnac and almond frangipane, brandy butter and brandy custard. And everything comes with idiot-proof step-by-step cooking and re-heating instructions.

They have thought of a vegetarian option: filo parcel with a julienne of vegetables with a fresh tomato and basil sauce. And if you are less than ten people, they suggest an option of roast stuffed duck with prunes in Armagnac and apple sauce. At Home's service does not come cheap – it works out at £45 per head – but the quality is undeniable. And if you are very busy, cannot face stuffing your own turkey or, as they say in their sales leaflet, 'you want to sparkle at Christmas' and can afford it, why not let them take the strain?

Fish

Cornish Fish Direct

The Pilchard Works, Tolcarne, Newlyn, Cornwall, TR18 5QH
Tel: 01327 263438 Fax: 01327 263438
email: pilchards@connections.co.uk
Contact: William Black.Last orders: 16 December. Switch, MasterCard, Visa.
Delivery charge: £9 for up to 10kg.

Cornish Fish Direct will send fish anywhere in mainland Britain by overnight delivery, and it is delivered before noon the next day. It offers prime fish, in peak condition and, whenever possible, caught sustainably. 'We feel that fish is fresher and in better condition when caught by inshore boats,' explained William Black. 'Also large trawlers that fish offshore in deeper waters tend to damage the sea beds with their nets. The fish are bounced around in the nets, so they can suffer skin graze. And the mesh size of the nets means too many juvenile fish are grabbed up. Inshore fleets, on the other hand, can be far more selective in what they catch as they favour line fishing with their catch often landed alive. We keep no stock of our own, but buy direct from the markets on a daily basis, at either Newlyn or other smaller Cornish ports, and try to despatch the fish on the same day as it is landed.'

At Christmas time the seas can be very rough, which makes it difficult for the smaller inshore boats to leave harbour. However, it is not only the weather but also the availability of Cornish-landed species that can make fish supplies 'a little awkward' at this time of year. For the main meal, William recommends Dover sole: 'great and roe-less between November through to Christmas.' They weigh 350 to 450g, so you should allow one per person. Fish can be filleted, skinned or prepared in any other way you want: it is like using a 'fishmonger on the phone'. Another suggestion that I find particularly appealing is a whole monkfish tail. These can weigh anything from 500g to 4kg. Once skinned and boned, and cut lengthways into two fillets, you can stuff the centre, tie it up, roast it and carve it exactly as you would any boneless joint. It cannot fail to satisfy any fish lover.

As prices are set on a daily rate by the market, at the time of going to press William was unable to predict them; but he is more than willing to discuss any order if you ring him up.

The Fresh Food Co

326 Portobello Road, London W10 5RU

Tel: 0181 969 0351 Fax: 0181 969 8050 email: organic@freshfood.co.uk

Contact: Thoby Young. Last orders: 12 December. Switch, Delta, MasterCard, Visa, Amex. Delivery charge: prices include p&p.

Sourcing their fish from Cornwall, the Fresh Food Company offers a 'bespoke' service for Christmas and recommends turbot, scallops or live lobsters. Also worth considering are the fish boxes. An Introductory Box costs £39.95, and although I find it difficult to pin them down as to exact quantities, I am assured it will include lemon sole, monkfish, scallops, and 1 to 2lb of 'family' fish such as whiting and white fish such as cod, plaice or haddock. At the top end of the scale is the Prime Catch at £59.95 for between 7 and 10lb of fish. This promises just prime fish species such as Dover sole, turbot or brill, but as they buy what is available on the day, they will not necessarily specify the species.

The Market Fish Shop

The Old Market, Victoria Road, Dartmouth, Devon, TQ6 9SE

Tel: 01803 832782

Contact: Jenny Rothery. Last orders: 12 December. Delivery charge: £10 for up to 10kg.

Recently the Market Fish Shop has set up a bespoke service supplying fish lovers all over Britain by overnight delivery. Fish is bought at auction from Brixham market, preferably from inshore boats. As Jenny Rothery says, 'their fish is day-landed and tends to be fresher'. Availability and price are subject to 'a nice run of weather', but Jenny is happy to discuss your order, tell you what is in season, fillet the fish if required, and send it vacuum-packed. 'It travels better, keeps longer and is much easier for freezing.'

For Christmas she recommends turbot, whole monkfish tails, or individual Dover soles weighing between 14 and 16oz on the bone or a large fish of 2 to 3lb 'that fillets nicely'. Lemon sole are also good at this time of year, and Jenny will supply them prepped *à la bonne femme*, meaning filleted, skinned and rolled up so they stay well tucked in. 'A gentle portion is two fillets per person, although the boys might go for three or four. They make a good starter, particularly if served with a sprinkling of green grapes for sole *Veronique*'.

On the basis that the colder the weather the better the shellfish, lobsters and crabs are also a good buy. A lobster will set you back about £8.50 per pound and a decent-sized Shanker crab with its big claws that weighs around 2½lb will cost around £10. Shellfish cannot be vacuum-packed, so they are sent in ice in a polystyrene box. Jenny will supply split uncooked lobsters, but shellfish are mainly sold ready boiled.

Vegetarian

Mrs Tee's Wild Mushroom

Gorse Meadow, Sway Road, Lymington, Hampshire, SO41 8LR

Tel: 01590 673354 Fax: 01590 673336

email: 106225.2141@compuserve.com

Contact: Brigitte Tee-Hillman. Last orders: 21 December. Delivery charge: p&p extra.

Mrs Tee is known in the trade as Mrs Mushroom and she has been collecting wild mushrooms in the New Forest since 1978. What started as a hobby has 'mushroomed' into a business, and now she supplies several top chefs with such own-picked or imported fresh fungi as chanterelles, ceps, chicken o' the woods and *pieds de moutons*.

She specialises in making up selections. At this time of year some mushrooms will be imported while others, she claims, can still be found locally. Mixtures include *girolles*, *chanterelles gris*, *chanterelles jaunes*, *pieds de mouton*, oyster, Forest ears and semi-wild *shi-itake*. Prices depend on the selection, but expect to pay between £4 and £5 per 4oz.

If you prefer to use dried mushrooms – and some cooks claim their flavour is far more intense – Mrs Tee also has a good supply. Best for soups, stews, risotto or a pasta sauce, soak them in hot water to soften before cooking and, for extra flavour, remember to add the soaking water as well while you are cooking. Packed in 100g bags, they come as mixed wild mushrooms at £5, ceps at £10 and (the rarest of them all) morels in 50g bags at £12.50.

Taste of the Wild

31 London Stone Estate, Broughton Street, London, SW8 3QJ

Tel: 0171 498 5654 Fax: 0171 498 5419

Contact: Alistair Lomax. Last orders: 19 December. MasterCard, Visa, Amex, Diners. Delivery charge: carriage free for orders in Central London and over £100; otherwise £10 per order; minimum order £20.

As its name suggests, Taste of the Wild supplies wild foods. At this time of year, however, own-gathered are a bit thin on the ground, so most of what is sold will be imported from all over the world.

Vegetarians, nonetheless, will appreciate the selection of mushrooms as a more than viable alternative to the bird. These can arrive rather glamorously packed in a wicker basket, but unless you intend to give it as a present (and a very good one it is too, costing £35 for a 1kg assortment), I would suggest you go for the loose mixture costing around £20 per kilo. Exactly which species this contains depends on current availability, but the chances are there will be chanterelles, *trompettes de la mort* (horn of plenty), *pieds de mouton* (hedgehog fungus), *pieds bleu*s (blewits), as well as such cultivated wild mushrooms as oyster and *shi-itake*.

The simplest and most effective way to cook them is to sauté them, and you should do this at the last moment, while making the gravy. The only preparation they need is a quick wipe and careful slicing. Then, in a mixture of half olive oil, half butter, cook them gently with some crushed garlic and chopped fresh parsley for no more than a few minutes, adding a dash of red wine just before they are ready. Serve them spooned onto a pre-baked filo pastry case or some grilled country bread lightly brushed with olive oil. Any vegetarian should be delighted.

Tideford Foods

Higher Tideford Farm, Cornworthy, Totnes, Devon, TQ9 7HL

Tel: 01803 712276 Fax: 01803 712388 email: tideford@shines.swis.net

Contact: Diana Cooper. Last orders: 15 December. No credit cards. Delivery charge: £6 for up to 10kg.

As a one-time vegetarian, Diane Cooper understands what it feels like to sit down to no more than a plate of vegetables for a Christmas lunch because no one remembered, or had the time, to prepare a vegetarian alternative.

Hence her chestnut and cranberry loaf, made with whole and puréed chestnuts and cranberries mixed together with wholemeal breadcrumbs, yoghurt and eggs. It arrives ready cooked and frozen, so all you need do is re-heat it and serve it with its cranberry and orange sauce. A 600g loaf costs £6.50, so there can be no possible excuse for any vegetarian feeling left out this year.

The Trimmings

Anybody who has spent hours trying to peel fresh chestnuts will know what a fiddly, frustrating job that is. Far better to save your time and buy them ready to use. The best on the market come from the Corrèze region near the Dordogne in south-west France. With all the work done for you, these are cooked, peeled and vacuum-packed plump whole chestnuts with the added advantage of not falling apart when you mix them into a stuffing. Imported by the Merchant Gourmet, you should find them in most good food shops, and you can telephone 0345 585168 for your nearest stockist. Failing that, you can mail order them from the Teesdale Trencherman on 01833 638370. A 200g (7oz) vacuum pack costs £2.50. But be warned: there is a hefty charge of £2.50 for postage and packing.

The Bay Tree Food Company

Lower Westcombe Farm, Evercreech, Shepton Mallet, Somerset, BA4 6ER

Tel: 01749 831300 Fax: 01749 831233 email: thebaytree@dial.pipex.com

Contact: Lucie Green. Last orders: 7 December. Switch, Delta, MasterCard, Visa. Delivery charge: p&p extra.

One of the traditions at my Christmas table is to serve pickled pears with goose. For years I have been making them as I was not aware I could buy them, but the good news is that the Bay Tree Food Company now produce them. I assure you, they are every bit as good as my own-made. Miniature whole baby velvet-soft peeled pears (I never bothered to peel mine) are poached in a light white wine vinegar syrup spiced with ginger and mixed spices, and cost £5.50 for a 380g kilner jar. They also do an appealing caramelised apple compôte, with its slices of apple in a buttery purée spiked with thyme, costing £4 for a 500g jar.

If, this year, you want a cranberry relish with a difference to go with either hot or cold turkey, try their cranberry and grapefruit relish costing £2.95 for 310g jar. With a loose, almost runny set, the fruity sauce is livened up with chopped almonds. Raspberry vinegar is boiled with cranberries for the smoother-textured cranberry and raspberry, and this costs £4.95 for 200g.

Eastbrook Farm Organic Meats

Bishopstone, Swindon, Wiltshire, SN6 18PW

Tel: 01793 790460 Fax: 01793 791239

email: eastbrookfarm@compuserve.com

Contact: Deborah Archer. Last orders: 5 December. Switch, Delta, MasterCard, Visa. Delivery charge: £10 for orders under £35; £8 for £35–75; £4 for £75–150; over £150, carriage free.

Helen Browning's passion is her pigs. To visit them free-ranging on the hills, with their arks as shelter, is to see very happy fully outdoor-reared animals. Saddlebacks, easily recognised by their bold pink stripe against black, 'make great mums', so Helen told me. 'And one of the reasons why some outdoor pig units fail is that they don't use the right pig. You can't expect a modern hybrid pig to know instinctively how to rear its young. They roll over and squash them. That's just one of the reasons we chose an old-fashioned breed.'

Another reason is the quality and flavour of the meat. The organic pork (to Soil Association standards) is markedly well textured with a fresh, earthy flavour. Equally good are the gluten-free organic sausages. Made from 80-per-cent Saddleback meat mixed with brown rice flour as a binder and stuffed into natural skins, the most popular to go with the bird are the pork chipolatas. Flavoured with mace, ginger, salt and pepper, quite coarse in texture, they cost £6.70 per kilo and come as long thin sausages with the small cocktail ones on request.

Their 'dead plain' coarsely cut organic sausage meat, at £6.70 per 500g, makes a good base for stuffing. As for keeping the bird moist, try the dry-cured unsmoked bacon cured from organic pork (it cannot be called organic bacon as saltpetre is used) that costs £13.49 a kilo.

The Fresh Food Co

326 Portobello Road, London W10 5RU

Tel: 0181 969 0351 Fax: 0181 969 8050 email: organic@freshfood.co.uk
Contact: Thoby Young. Last orders: 12 December. Switch, Delta, MasterCard, Visa, Amex. Delivery charge: prices include p&p.

If the thought of shopping for vegetables – and organic ones at that – daunts you, you could order up a Christmas box from the Fresh Food Company. Unlike other vegetable box suppliers they offer a nation-wide service, so you can have it delivered almost anywhere in mainland Britain.

The Fresh Food Company buys in its produce from all over the world, and for the Christmas box offers in the region of 25 lines of fruit, vegetables, root vegetables, herbs, salads and nuts. 'The nature of our service,' says Thoby Young, 'is that our customers trust us to buy on their behalf.' What that means in terms of choice I am not quite sure, but if you are not satisfied you can rest assured that they offer an unconditional 'no quibble' money-back guarantee for dissatisfied customers. The Christmas box with an approximate weight of 30lb costs around £50.

Heal Farm Meats

Kings Nympton, Umberleigh, Devon, EX37 9TB

Tel: 01769 574341 Fax: 01769 572839

Contact: Anne Petch. Last orders: 9 December. Switch, Delta, MasterCard, Visa. Delivery charge: £8.50 for any order.

Anne Petch started business by rearing rare-breed pigs. Then she started an on-farm butchery unit to process the meat, and like all good ventures it has grown and grown.

At Christmas time, there is no end to what Anne has on offer. To go with her hams (see page 132) or indeed the free-range turkeys grown for her on the edge of Dartmoor, there is Cumberland Sauce made with port, red currant jelly, fresh oranges and spices that she describes as 'a thin pouring sauce – only one step away from pouring port'. Cranberry and Orange is 'stiffer and more like a relish', and Spiced Preserved Oranges are cut into fairly thick slices, and simmered in a sugar syrup with mace, cloves and cinnamon. All these preserves are packed in 340ml jars, and cost around £5.75.

You can buy 500g packs of her rare-breed streaky bacon with its layer of rich fat for basting the bird, and chipolatas to go around it. With a meat content of 85 per cent, these are made with coarsely-ground shoulder meat mixed with hard back fat and occasionally belly, and filled into natural casings. The most popular flavours are plain, or pork and herb, although you can order them with garlic, or tomato and chilli. A 1kg pack contains 30 to 35 sausages, and costs £6.24.

Anne is understandably proud of her stuffings, made on-farm in the butchery unit with fresh ingredients. She likes to 'ring the changes', inventing new ones each year. This year, expect to find parsley and lemon, ' a family recipe made with loads of parsley, thyme, lemon juice and zest, brown breadcrumbs, egg and suet for the neck end of poultry'. For the cavity Anne suggests a chestnut forcemeat made with sausage meat, onions and chestnut purée. Then there is a hazelnut and ginger that is recommended for pork or goose, and a Persian fruit made with dried fruits, nuts and spices.

If you order the Turkey Kit, all the choosing is done for you. A large kit contains 500g each of lemon and parsley stuffing, chestnut forcemeat, streaky bacon and plain chipolatas. It costs £13.13, and is recommended for a bird weighing over 5½kg. And there's a small kit containing exactly half the weights costing £6.57.

Holly Tree Farm Shop

Chester Road, Tabley, Knutsford, Cheshire, WA16 0EU

Tel: 01565 651835 Fax: 01565 651835 email: bailey@hollytree.u-net.com

Contact: Karol Bailey. Last orders: 15 December. No credit cards. Delivery charge: £12.50 for up to 10kg.

What with all the geese, ducks and turkeys Karol Bailey and her husband rear and pluck (see pages 35 and 39), I don't know how she finds the time to make Christmas stuffings as well. But they are certainly worth ordering to go with her birds, and come in handy, flat1lb packs, ideal for freezing. You can easily break off as much as you need and then return the pack to the freezer.

Only fresh herbs and breadcrumbs are used for the base, and there is a choice of four flavours: dried apricot and parsley, rosemary and orange, spicy plum, and orchard: a mixture of apples from her garden, celery and almonds. Fully flavoured but not overpoweringly so, these are well textured and a welcome adjunct to any bird.

I admit I have not tried all Karol's sausages, particularly since her range has grown to 30 in number over the last year. Some are a bit fanciful (turkey and pineapple does not grab me). On the other hand, pork with fresh green and red peppers was a triumph. On the day, it is probably best to stick with a simpler sausage with so many flavours competing elsewhere, so I recommend her pork and chive chipolatas. With a 90-per-cent meat content, made from own-reared pigs and stuffed into natural skins, expect about 20 to the pound.

Mooreland Foods
Vost Farm, Morley Green, Wilmslow, Cheshire, SK9 5NU
Tel: 01625 548499 Fax: 01625 548606
Contact: John Ward. Last orders: 10 December. Switch, Delta, MasterCard, Visa, Amex, Diners. Delivery charge: £6.50 for overnight carriage; minimum order £25.

If you are ordering from Mooreland Foods (see pages 21 and 132), ask them to add a pack of their Cheshire bacon for laying on top of the turkey. Dry-cured, it is a plain, unadorned bacon that is certain not to splutter, shrink or weep over the turkey's breast. I recommend a pack of middle, £2.15 for 8–12oz, with its long rashers of meaty back with the streaky attached so you also get the benefit of the fat. Because it is relatively salty, you may want to cut down on the seasoning for the bird; and personally I would go for green (unsmoked) bacon as the flavour of the smoke might overpower the bird.

Mrs Huddleston's Luxury Home-made Provisions
13 The Green, Mentmore, Buckinghamshire, LU7 0QF
Tel: 01296 661423 Fax: 01296 661423
email: 10072.3646@compuserve.com
Contact: Christine Huddleston. Last orders: 4 December. No credit cards. Delivery charge: £3.50 minimum.

How do I find the best food producers? The answer is in all sorts of different ways. Loading up the car with maps and Violet (my dog) and setting off for an explore, or following up recommendations from other food lovers, are just two.

Dr Julian Cowley of Bedfordshire was kind enough to write to me singing the praises of Christine Huddleston for 'her excellent conserves (produced) at her delightful cottage'. Further research proved Dr Cowley to be spot on. So I take much pleasure in recommending her cranberry and apple sauce or cranberry relish. Both are made with cranberries, spices ('predominantly cinnamon'), and lemon with apples added for the sauce. The major difference is texture; the former has a lighter set and is of a thinner consistency than the latter. Both have a bursting fruitiness, a good balance of sharp to sweet, and cost £2.50 for a 8oz jar.

Richard Woodall

Lane End, Waberthwaite, Nr Millom, Cumbria, LA19 5YJ

Tel: 01229 717237 Fax: 01229 717007

Contact: Richard Woodall. Last orders: 5 December. MasterCard, Visa. Delivery charge: 5kg or less, £4.70; over 5kg, £6.

There are all number of tips for cooking a turkey so that the breast stays moist. Turning it upside down or covering it with a piece of muslin (a J-cloth will do) soaked in butter are just a couple of suggestions. I usually start with my bird on its back, then turn it the right way up for the last hour, covering it with rashers of bacon. But you have to be careful about which bacon you use; a poor quality one shrinks to nothing and weeps scum all over the breast, leaving unfortunate tide-marks and a softened skin behind.

Richard Woodall's bacon behaves impeccably. Sold in 250g and 500g packs, unsmoked streaky (Richard's preferred cut) costs £1.35 for 250g and £2.59 for 500g. Dry-cured for a rasping flavour, it neither shrinks nor splutters. And it has the added advantage of intra-muscular and outer-layer fat, so it promises to keep a turkey's breast good and moist. A couple of points though: stick with the green (unsmoked) or it may overpower the flavour of the turkey; and cut down on the amount of salt you rub into the skin, as his bacon is relatively salty.

The Scottish Gourmet

Thistle Mill, Biggar, Strathclyde, ML12 6LP

Tel: 01899 221268 Fax: 01899 220456

Contact: Gillian Bell. Last orders: 8 December. Switch, MasterCard, Visa, Amex, Diners. Delivery charge: £6.85; over eight items, p&p free.

The Scottish Gourmet, a subscription mail-order food club with an emphasis on Scottish recipes and produce (see page 180), really does make life easy at Christmas time and throughout the year.

Bored with peeling vegetables? Then throw away the peeler and order up a choice of their gourmet vegetables. Using old-fashioned varieties with taste, they prepare carrots cooked with onions in a marsala and double-cream sauce, leeks braised in red elderberry wine with garlic and coriander, and chipped parsnips with parsley and honey. A portion of each for two people costs £5.45, and £9.68 for four. Scottish potatoes are transformed into colcannon made with red rather than green cabbage, and *pommes Anna* made with cream, egg, thyme and spring onions, costing £7.87 for two portions of each.

They also prepare a stuffing and trimming pack costing £10.95. This contains two packs of chipolatas, one pack of streaky bacon from Ramsay of Carluke, and three stuffings each weighing 280g. These are in three flavour: pork, sage and oatmeal; lamb, mint and oatmeal; and skirlie, made from spring onions, oatmeal and duck fat. And if you think that still leaves you too much work to do, you could always order your entire Christmas meal from the Scottish Gourmet. The menu this year is a soup (which one is not yet certain), oven-ready pheasant with skirlie stuffing, prepared vegetables and a traditional clootie dumpling.

Taste of the Wild

31 London Stone Estate, Broughton Street, London, SW8 3QJ

Tel: 0171 498 5654 Fax: 0171 498 5419

Contact: Alistair Lomax. Last orders: 19 December. MasterCard, Visa, Amex, Diners. Delivery charge: carriage free for orders in Central London and over £100; otherwise £10 per order; minimum order £20.

Taste of the Wild imports a selection of baby vegetables grown in France under plastic, so if you are no great fan of Brussels sprouts, this year you might welcome a change.

They come carefully packed in punnets weighing 300g, costing mostly £10.50 each. Used by several top restaurants, these are vegetables at their most infantile and tender; but be warned, on no account will they split a punnet for a private customer. Favourites are the punnets of about 60 tiny carrots no more than 3 inches long, or 30 turnips the size of golf balls, or 20 baby fennel. Forgive me if I am stating the obvious, but do remember that vegetables as small and tender as these need no more than the gentlest and quickest of cooking.

Chestnut and Parsnip Stuffing

This excellent, light, aromatic stuffing, which works well with both turkey and goose, comes from *Sainsbury's Christmas Book* by Josceline Dimbleby.

Serves 8–10

20g (¾oz) dried wild mushrooms
50g (2oz) butter

15 ml (1 tbsp) olive oil
4cm (1½in) piece ginger, peeled and finely chopped
4 garlic cloves, finely chopped
375g (13oz) parsnips, peeled and finely chopped
50g (2oz) dried apricots, finely chopped
450g (1lb) chestnuts, roughly chopped
50g (2oz) walnuts, roughly chopped
1 egg, beaten
Salt and freshly ground black pepper

Put the mushrooms in a bowl with 150ml (¼pt) hot water and soak for about 2 hours. Melt the butter and oil in a frying pan, add the parsnips and stir for about 10 minutes until soft. Add the ginger and garlic and stir for about 1 minute. Turn up the heat, and add the apricots and mushrooms with their soaking liquid. Leave to bubble, without stirring, for 2 minutes until almost all the liquid is absorbed, and turn into a mixing bowl. Add the chestnuts and walnuts, stir in the egg and season generously. Leave to cool before stuffing the bird.

Wendy Brandon

Felin Wen, Boncath, Pembrokeshire, SA37 OJR

Tel: 01239 841568 Fax: 01239 841746

Contact: Wendy Brandon. Last orders: 15 December. MasterCard, Visa.
Delivery charge: £5.75 for any size order.

Wendy Brandon came to preserve-making relatively late in life. From a delightful picture-postcard converted stone mill in the depths of Wales, she runs a successful business making some of our most innovative jams and pickles.

From her 'Green-label' range (meaning no salt and no added sugar) comes a vibrantly flavoured Cranberry and Orange (made with whole fresh oranges), or plain Cranberry preserve. Instead of sugar, Wendy adds concentrated apple juice. 'They take longer to make, and longer to reach a set as the juice takes longer to evaporate. But the preserves have a much more concentrated flavour as they are all fruit and juice. Nothing else. A 100-per-cent fruit content. And for every kilo of preserve there's about one and half kilos of fruit.' Bursting with fruit and relatively runny in set, a 225g jar costs £2.90 and should serve at least six people.

The Christmas Pudding

The cost of £3.99 strikes me as exceptionally good value for a box of six silver tiny pudding charms, just over 1cm (½in) long or tall. The selection from Hawkin by Post, St Margaret, Harleston, Norfolk, IP20 0PJ (Tel: 01986 782536, Fax: 01986 782468) is made up of a horseshoe, bell, duck, cat, pig and elephant. And as for being 'real' silver, they come with a charming disclaimer: 'The metal is intended to be at least 93 per cent silver but production is very much a 'cottage industry' and this cannot be guaranteed. However it really doesn't matter, since these are something where traditionally price is more important than quality. But nowadays the law says you must be warned.' And warned you have been.

The Carved Angel Ltd

2 South Embankment, Dartmouth, Devon, TQ6 9DH

Tel: 01803 832465 Fax: 01803 835141

Contact: Joyce Molyneux. Last orders: 17 December. MasterCard, Visa. Delivery charge: £3.50.

Joyce Molyneux is one of my favourite cooks. I admire her constant search for the very best local produce, and the simplicity and clarity of her dishes.

From her restaurant she sells jars of own-made jam, marmalade, pickles ('whatever I feel like with whatever is in season'), and at Christmas own-made puddings. Of the hearty, fruity variety, they contain masses of muscat raisins, sultanas, diced fresh apple, fresh orange and lemon juice and rind, eggs, preserved ginger, nutmeg, mace, flour, soft breadcrumbs, beef suet and a liberal dose of brandy. Soft in texture and wonderfully rich – due no doubt to the beef suet – they are good and dark even though Joyce and her kitchen staff only start making in September. A 2lb pudding, the only size Joyce makes, costs £10 and comes wrapped in calico for a proper boiling cloth. If you pick it up from the restaurant or any of her stockists (Clarkes, 122 Kensington Church Street, London W8 4BH, Tel: 0171 229 2190, or Whites, The Square, Winchester, Hampshire SO23 9EX, Tel: 01962 840805), it comes packed in an earthenware basin. Otherwise, if you order by post, I am afraid you will only get a plastic basin.

Chatsworth Farm Shop

Stud Farm, Pilsley, Bakewell, Derbyshire, DE45 1UF

Tel: 01246 583392 Fax: 01246 583464

Contact: Sandy Boyd.Last orders: 14 December. Switch, Visa, Amex. Delivery charge: £9.50 for all next-day fresh delivieries.

I find it very reassuring that the Christmas pudding sold at the Chatsworth Farm Shop is made to the House recipe. If it good enough for the Duke and Duchess, then it must be very good.

Nicely textured and lighter than several I have tried, its ingredients are the usual vine fruits plus almonds and, rather unusually, dates, stout, sugar, golden syrup, eggs, fresh orange and lemon juice and zest, breadcrumbs, wheat flour and brandy. And, because it is made with vegetarian suet, it is suitable for vegetarians. Made in 150g, 450g, 900g and 2kg sizes, they cost £2.95, £5.75. £7.50 and £18.50 respectively. It is fruity in both texture and taste.

Church Farmhouse Cakes
Croxton Kerrial, Grantham, Lincolnshire, NG32 1QP
Tel: 01476 870150
Contact: Julie Duff. Last orders: 5 December. No credit cards. Delivery charge: p&p extra

Normally I do not like my mincemeat 'messed' around. As far as I am concerned it should be plain and simple, full of fruit and reeking of brandy. But I have to say that Julie Duff's mincemeats could persuade me otherwise. Inventive, while relatively restrained, nicely balanced and textured, these are certainly mincemeats with a difference.

Made in three varieties, they all contain vine fruit, vegetarian suet, dark sugars and (for the allergic) no nuts. 'Seriously Fruity' is a blend of figs, dates and plums (prunes) laced with brandy, which she describes as 'old-fashioned and rich of the type eaten in Victorian times'. 'Delectable Apricot', made from dried apricots, fresh orange juice and grated rind flavoured with rum and Cointreau, is far paler in colour and lighter in flavour. 'Festive Rich and Spicy', with glacé cherries, is dark and sweet, and reeks of cherry brandy. Matured for six months to 'sit and mull away nicely', these mincemeats are packed in prettily labelled 12oz glass jars, and cost £3.25.

The Country Victualler
Winkburn Hall, Newark, Nottinghamshire, NG22 8PQ
Tel: 01636 636465 Fax: 01636 636717 email: @alderton.co.uk
Contact: Richard Craven-Smith-Milnes. MasterCard, Visa, Amex, Diners. Last orders: 15 December. Delivery charge: for orders under £50, £10.

Richard Craven-Smith-Milnes' grandmother lived in Scrutton Hall, Scrutton, Yorkshire. Her Christmas puddings acquired a formidable reputation in the area, with neighbouring country houses eagerly awaiting their seasonal hamper. So when Richard set up a food business, it seemed only right and proper that he should make them. A stickler for tradition, he follows the recipe to the ingredient. They include the usual vine fruits, apples, mixed peel, nuts, spices, brandy, rum, breadcrumbs, eggs, flour and suet. The suet is, of course, beef suet because that is how Grandmother made her puddings, and he sees no reason to change it. Anyway, 'vegetarian suet lacks "something" – the puddings are not as good'. If he has any regrets about the inclusion of beef suet, they are purely on the grounds that he can longer export his puddings to France; the French along with the rest of Europe will not accept any product with beef derivatives.

Matured for six months, Richard's puddings are very dark, very shiny, gloriously rich, and veer towards the solid state; which is how they like them in Yorkshire. The largest, a sturdy 3lb 10oz, costs £15.26 and comes in a proper china pudding basin. The 2lb at £8.10 and 1lb at £4.92 are packed in plastic bowls. That, as far as I can find out, is his only concession to modern times.

James Chocolates

Lower Westcombe Farm, Shepton Mallet, Somerset, BA4 6ER

Tel: 01749 831311 Fax: 01749 831233

Contact: James Hutchins. Last orders: 14 December. Delivery charge: p&p extra.

I am told that serious chocolate lovers regard the pudding as an unwelcome distraction; something to be waded through before the real business begins. A solution would be to serve them James's chocolate truffle Christmas pudding as the pudding, then no-one could possibly complain.

Made with a *ganache* of fresh cream, and a good French couverture into which dried fruits soaked in brandy, candied peel and roasted almonds are folded, the mixture is then doused with yet more brandy and judiciously spiced with the traditional Christmas spices. James hand-rolls this into a mini-pudding about 2 inches in diameter, dips this in dark chocolate, dribbles some white chocolate over the top to look like the cream, and then decorates it with green marzipan leaves and red sugar berries.

Costing £1.95, a 2-inch chocolate truffle Christmas pudding should be quite enough for even the most dedicated fan. They are sumptuously rich. But you never know. In which case James, ever keen to oblige, will make them larger to order.

John Pimblett & Sons Ltd

College Bakery, College Street, St Helens, Merseyside, WA10 1TP

Tel: 01744 28644 Fax: 01744 454027

Contact: John Pimblett. Last orders: 15 December. Switch, Delta, MasterCard, Visa. Delivery charge: £5.25 up to 5kg .

Chris Johnson runs the excellent Ramsbottom Victuallers, a small food shop in Ramsbottom, not far from Manchester. He makes a point of sourcing from the best suppliers, so when he trumpeted the glories of Pimblett's Christmas pudding, I knew I was onto a good thing. As Chris says: 'It's moist, fruity, dark and rich. Everything you'd expect from a Christmas pudding and better than any I've ever tried. That's probably because it's got more suet in than most. When you steam it you see it oozing out. It works as it's so wonderfully moist.'

Now this is a tricky subject. Most producers have cut down on the quantity and/or opted for a vegetarian suet. Not so John Pimblett. He clings to his beef suet, as it is what gives his pudding an extra deep flavour, and he is right. (Incidentally he also admits to sneaking a touch of lard into some of his breads – but that is another matter.) John does admit to having doubts about whether some people might find the beef suet unacceptable in these controversial animal-fat times, but it strikes me that if you do want a traditional product, traditionally made with traditional ingredients, then beef suet is what you go for. If some customers shy away, then so be it.

In fact, Pimblett's puddings are so fruity, sticky and robust, they remind me of a plum duff. Made with all the right ingredients, such as vine fruits, Bramley apples, eggs, milk, nutmeg, cinnamon and cloves, they come in two sizes, 465g at £6.50 and 925g at £8.50, and are certainly not for the faint hearted.

Meg Rivers Cakes

Middle Tysoe, Warwickshire, CV35 0SE

Tel: 01295 688101 Fax: 01295 680799

Contact: Meg Rivers. Last orders: 12 December. Switch, Delta, MasterCard, Visa. Delivery charge: £2.95 per delivery address.

Meg Rivers is very particular about the ingredients she uses for her cakes and biscuits. Now she has carried her preoccupations into her lines of Christmas puddings. Apart from the traditional pudding that has all the usual ingredients, I was drawn by the sound of her 'alternative' Christmas pudding. Described as for 'those who prefer a pudding containing the lighter fruits', its ingredients are listed as pineapple, sultanas, apricots, orange and lemon peel, cherries (red, yellow and green), ginger, sugar, almonds, vegetable suet, organic wheat flour, white breadcrumbs, fresh apple, figs, eggs, fresh orange and lemon juice, brandy, salt and cinnamon. It sounds light, fruity and rather interesting, and costs £7.50 for 450g or £10.50 for 900g. I think I may try one this year.

Mrs Gill's Country Cakes

Unit 5, Link House, Leat Street, Tiverton, Devon, EX16 5LG

Tel: 01884 242744 Fax: 01884 257440

Contact: Jacqueline Gill. Last orders: 5 December. No credit cards. Delivery charge: p&p extra.

When it comes to Christmas pudding, the ingredients are more or less set in stone. So when judging their quality the questions to ask are:

what is the quality and quantity of vine fruits used; does it have flour, vegetable or animal suet; how sweet is it; what is its texture like; and how laced with alcohol is it?

Jacqueline Gill's Christmas puddings are nicely rich, dense, reasonably heavy, very fruity and have certainly seen their fair share of the bottle. She makes them using good quality and plenty of sultanas, raisins, currants, mixed peel, and glacé cherries (an addition that I do not altogether agree with). Then she adds fresh wholemeal bread-crumbs, flour, muscovado sugar, a choice of vegetarian or beef suet, eggs, mixed spices, ale and sherry. Matured for at least two months, they come in sizes ranging from ½lb costing £3.95 up to 4lb costing £12.75, and have an abundance of flavour that strikes me as the hallmark of all Jacqueline's products.

Pengoon Farm

Nancegollan, Helston, Cornwall, TR13 0BH

Tel: 01326 561219

Contact: Edna East. Last orders: 15 December. No credit cards. Delivery charge: prices include p&p.

Instead of the more traditional brandy or Cumberland butter, can I recommend serving the Christmas pudding and mince pies with clotted cream? The clotted cream that Edna East of Pengoon Farm makes is special in that first, it is made with a rich buttery Jersey cream; secondly, the cream is not pasteurised, so the flavour is even richer and nuttier; and thirdly, it is made in the 'proper' old-fashioned way. Edna stands bowls of unpasteurised Jersey cream in pans of water on top of the stove to gently scald (cook) the cream. You need to take great care, because if you overdo the heat the cream turns gritty, but if it is not hot enough the cream is bland. If you have never seen the process, it is fascinating. At first nothing seems to happen; then, as the cream slowly condenses, tiny bubbles start breaking at the top, pitting it like the surface of the moon. Suddenly it turns golden, forms a thick honey-comb crust and – hey presto! – it is clotted.

Sold in 100g (4oz) cartons costing £1.90 and 8oz cartons costing £2.90, clotted cream has, so Edna reckons, a shelf-life of about seven days provided it is kept cool. You can freeze it, although it will lose some of its texture. One possible disadvantage is that, because it is made in bowls, when potting it up the crust tends to get mixed into the body of the cream rather than staying on the top.

Rocombe Farm Fresh Ice Cream Ltd

Middle Rocombe Farm, Stoke in Teignhead, Newton Abbot, Devon, TQ12 4QL

Tel: 01626 872291 Fax: 01626 873645 email: rocombe@premier.co.uk

Contact: Peter and Suzanne Redstone. Last orders: 5 December. MasterCard, Visa. Delivery charge: prices include p&p.

Ice cream by mail order – surely some mistake? No, Rocombe Farm will send their rich, luscious, creamy and very pure ice cream anywhere on the UK mainland by overnight delivery. It arrives packed in a white styrofoam box surrounded by dry ice, so it is guaranteed to arrive very firm indeed.

What is also unusual is the quality of the ice cream itself. Unlike virtually every other on-farm maker, they do not use stabilisers or emulsifiers. 'They are put in to hold the mix together, to trap the molecules of air and to give the ice cream texture and shelf-life,' Peter Redstone explains, 'but if you have a high enough fat content – and for the right texture it must be cream – and use eggs as we do, you don't need them. And because they aren't there, not only does it make ours a purer product but it also means it has that cleaner, clearer, fresher flavour.' Theirs is made with the best – and only the best – ingredients, with a basic mix of organic (to Soil Association standards) full-cream Jersey milk, double cream, unrefined cane sugar and organic free-range eggs. In other words, this is everything you would hope for in an ice-cream.

And if you think the ice cream is expensive – in comparison to several supermarket brands – it is. But another factor you have to take into account is the amount of added air (the technical term is over-run). You need it in an ice cream, or it would set rock hard. The question is how much? Some companies add as much as 120 per cent, but Rocombe Farm adds on average a mere 35 per cent. Obviously air comes cheap, so if you were to pump up an ice cream with air you could lower the price. But Rocombe Farm has opted for a dense mix. This is another reason why it is so good.

The ice-cream hampers are sold under the disconcerting title of Cool Yule with 3 Cool Choices [sic]. Each hamper contains a 1-litre tub of Christmas pudding ice cream made from fruits and nuts soaked in French brandy, plus five 500ml tubs of different flavours and costs £36.95. The Chocolate Lovers is made up of chocolate chip, Drambuie chocolate truffle, super chocolate chocolate chip, chocolate with balls (also known as Maltesers), and Rocombe Royale (a mixture of Grand Marnier with dark Belgian chocolate chip). Family Favourites contains all the well-known tried and tested flavours, such as lemon meringue (my favourite) and Crunchies 'n cream; and Organic is plainer and more restrained.

Serve them with – or as an alternative to – the Christmas pudding. They are simply scrumptious. Otherwise keep them in the freezer and dip into them as and when. Remember, though, to give them a good 10 to 15 minutes before serving, to soften them slightly.

Truffles

72 Belle Vue Road, Salisbury, Wiltshire, SP1 3YD

Tel: 01722 331978

Contact: Barbara Bayfield. Last orders: 10 December. No credit cards. Delivery charge: 80p for a 8oz pudding; 1lb, £1.30; 2lb, £2.80; 3lb, £4.20; 4lb, £5.60.

A one-time private cook, Barbara Bayfield supplies tea shops with various cakes and scones, but it is for her Traditional Olde English Plum (also know as Christmas) puddings that I single her out. Using her grandmother's old-fashioned and laborious recipe, she starts making in May through to 'the start of the summer holidays', so the puddings will have been aged for at least 6 months.

Working in her kitchen in 20 one-pound batches, 'for no other reason than it's easier for me that way', first vine fruits – sultanas, raisins and currants – are soaked overnight in a dark stout and medium cream sherry. Wholemeal breadcrumbs are crumbed in a food processor for each batch. They must be the right size: 'if they're too large they make holes in the puddings'. All these are mixed with beef suet (sunflower suet for the vegetarian version), muscovado sugar, glacé cherries, mixed peel, fresh eggs, mixed spices and plain white flour, 'even though I only use one pound for every 20 one-pound mixes. Wholemeal flour would make too heavy a pudding.' Then she adds copious amounts of stout and sherry, and pressure cooks the puddings for about 45 minutes for the 8oz size up to two hours for the 4lb size.

While still hot, the puddings are treated to a liberal dose of brandy or rum or Cointreau or Drambuie. 'If you add the liqueur before it is cooked, most of it boils away in the cooking. And when ordering, you can choose which you prefer.' Then they are stored until Christmas-time.

Packed in plastic bowls in sizes ranging from 8oz at £2.95, 1lb at £4.50, 2lb at £6.90, 3lb at £9.90 and 4lb at £12, the puddings come complete with heating instructions either for steaming or in a microwave. These are proper Christmas puddings: dense and quite stolid, substantially spiced and generously fruited. They demand to have room left for them after the main course.

The Village Bakery

Melmerby, Penrith, Cumbria, CA10 1HE

Tel: 01768 881515 Fax: 01768 881848 email: orders@village-bakery.com

Contact: Andrew Whitley. Switch, Delta, MasterCard, Visa, Diners. Last orders: 12 December. Delivery charge: £6 for orders under £20; £5 for £20–30; £4 for £30–60; over £60, carriage free.

Andrew Whitley produces, as far as I know, the only 100-per-cent organic Christmas pudding. Probably healthier than most, its recipe has not changed for 20 years,-which is as long as Andrew has been in business.

'We use minimal sugar, sunflower oil instead of suet (which anyway would melt when cooking, so oil works just as well) and it's not overloaded with alcohol. But it's very fruity,' he assured me, 'with the flavour coming mainly from the fruit and spices.'

First the raisins and sultanas are soaked in Golden Promise, an organic beer from the Caledonian Brewery, then mixed with fresh apple and oranges, wholemeal flour and wholemeal breadcrumbs, raw cane sugar, free-range eggs, cinnamon, nutmeg and mixed spices and, of course, sunflower oil. He steams them in his wood-fired oven in a what he calls a 'coffin' filled with water. The puddings stand on trivets above the water, heated by the dying embers after bread baking. The whole process takes about four hours, and he is proud that he is not wasting fuel or valuable resources to cook his puddings. Sold in sizes of 8oz at £3.15, 1lb at £5.80 and 2lb at £8.40, they are very wholesome.

To go with the puddings, there is Cumberland butter packed in 140g jars at £2.45. This is made in the time-honoured way by melting the butter, stirring in the sugar and rum and letting them set.'It makes for a heavy butter, but that's how it's made up here. People even spread it on bread or scones.'

Christmas Pudding Ice Cream

Serves 3–4

Here is a quick, simple method to make your own Christmas-pudding ice cream. As I imagine the last thing anybody wants to do over the holidays is to start from scratch and make ice cream, use a bought-in tub instead. Choose a good quality plain vanilla that is not too sweet.

About 575 ml (1pt) vanilla ice cream
About 140–170g (5–6oz) leftover Christmas pudding
20ml (1 generous tbsp) marmalade
15ml (1 tbsp) Cointreau
15–30ml (1–2 tbsp) brandy

Remove the ice cream from the freezer and allow it to soften slightly. Spoon or tip the pudding into a food processor and whizz for a few seconds. Scrape the pudding away from the sides of the bowl. Add the ice cream, marmalade, Cointreau and brandy. Whizz again. Transfer the mixture to a suitable container and freeze. Remove the ice cream from the freezer a few minutes before serving.

From *Fast Food for Friends* by Lewis Esson with Henrietta Green and Marie-Pierre Moine (Conran Octopus)

The Christmas Cake

Bonner's Handmade Kentish Cakes

The Museum of Kent Life, Cobtree Lock Lane, Sandling, Maidstone, Kent, ME14 3AU

Tel: 01622 663708 Fax: 01622 663708

Contact: Mary Bonner. Last orders: 3 December. No credit cards. Delivery charge: p&p extra.

If you have ever popped into the tea-rooms at the Museum of Kent Life near Maidstone, or the Historic Dockyard in Chatham, you will be familiar with Mary Bonner's baking. She researched, developed and adapted various old recipes to 'reflect Kentish life'. So popular have they proved that she now offers a mail-order service for a couple of her cakes.

The cider and apple cake is made using a local cider to soak the fruits, then Bramley apples (tinned, but Mary insists these work better than fresh) are mixed in with flour, eggs and sugar to make a fat-free, earthy cake. Ale cake is made to more or less the same recipe, but this time a local ale – either Shepherd Neame or Goachers – is used, as is a vegetable margarine.

Both cakes are decorated with nuts and fruit before baking, glazed with French brandy when they come out of the oven, cost £9 for a 10cm cake, and arrive wrapped in a gold band and boxed in a gold box. These are plain simple cakes that are best eaten relatively fresh rather than matured, but are none the worse for that.

The Christmas Cake

Flat 1, 17 Stanley Gardens, London W11 2NG

Tel: 0171 229 6722 Fax: 0171 229 6722

Contact: Sisi Edmiston. Last orders: 10 December. No credit cards. Personal shoppers only.

Sisi Edmiston's cakes look so good it almost seems a shame to cut into one. They are so generously and meticulously decorated with nuts and naturally dyed cherries that you could be forgiven for mistaking them for a table arrangement.

They are made to a family recipe that uses butter, unbleached flour, molasses, and masses of dried Australian sultanas, Californian raisins and Greek currants. First she soaks the fruit in vintage cognac, sherry, apricot brandy and fresh lime juice for at least seven days to plump it up, then she adds even more dried fruit such as apricots, dates, peaches, grated pineapple and grated carrots 'to give it colour', and nuts. Then she stirs in a minimal amount of unbleached flour to bind the mixture together, as 'the cakes are about 98 per cent fruit'; a little glycerine to keep them moist; and vanilla and almond essence for extra flavour.

The cakes are baked for about five and a half hours at an incredibly low temperature in a convection oven that, Sisi told me triumphantly, 'disproves Prue Leith's theory that you can't cook a cake in a convection oven'. Then they are matured for two months and finally laden with the fruit and nuts and glazed with a mixture of damson and apricot jam for a glistening finish. The result is as good to eat as it looks, with a texture more like a boiled than a traditionally baked fruit cake: moist, succulent and indeed very fruity. Sold in a variety of sizes and shapes, a 4-in square, fully decorated and boxed in a see-through box, costs £17.50. A 6-in round or square costs £35.

If you are tempted by the sound of Sisi's cakes, you will have to order and collect it from her, or starting in October she will be selling them at various Christmas fairs all over the country and you can ring her for details. Failing that, you can buy them at Fortnum and Mason in London.

Church Farmhouse Cakes

Croxton Kerrial, Grantham, Lincolnshire, NG32 1QP

Tel: 01476 870150

Contact: Julie Duff. Last orders: 5 December. No credit cards. Delivery charge: p&p extra.

Church Farmhouse Cakes is a farmhouse business in the true sense of the word, started about two years ago for her retirement by Julie Duff. Her cakes are made in her farmhouse kitchen, in small batches and, as she is keen to stress, 'stirred with a wooden spoon'.

Once the chef to the Duke and Duchess of Rutland, Julie has been making cakes since she was a child, and she still uses the same recipe that her grandmother gave her, 'only slightly adapted'. A committed member of the 'you only get out what you put in' school, Julie uses the best quality ingredients such as free-range eggs, plump vine fruits and butter.

For the Christmas Rich Brandy Fruit Cake, first Julie soaks all the vine fruits in a French brandy for 48 hours, then she mixes in the eggs, flour, dark brown sugar, black treacle, various spices such as nutmeg and allspice, natural coloured cherries and ground and chopped almonds. Slowly baked to keep them moist, the cakes are then matured for at least two months, 'probably a bit longer until you lose the taste of treacle and the cake just becomes rich'. Covered on top with a layer of almond paste and a layer of fondant icing, the cakes are hand decorated. This year promises hand-painted marzipan cut-outs of a plump red-breasted robin perched on a sprig of holly. A 5-inch cake weighing 900g costs £18.50, and a 7-inch cake (1.8kg) costs £26.50.

The Seriously Almond Christmas Cake is for lovers of almonds. A paler cake, it is made with Amaretto and light brown sugar rather than brandy and treacle, yellow and green cherries, extra almonds and a dash of almond oil. As you cut your first slice, the aroma of almonds is overwhelming and the flavour very pronounced. Completely covered with almond paste and stunningly – and very subtly – decorated with lightly toasted almond paste, holly leaves and bells edged with gold, it is baked in three sizes: a 4-in/500g cakes costs £14.50, a 5-in/900g costs £18.50, and a 7-in/1.8kg costs £26.50.

Finally there is an Orange and Cointreau Fruit cake. This time the fruit is soaked in Cointreau with added fresh orange juice and zest, and it is decorated with baked orange slices. A 5-in/900g cake costs £15.50 and a 7-in/1.8kg costs £22.50.

Incidentally, all Julie's cakes come tied with a bow and boxed in dark green boxes for a good present, assuming you can resist the temptation to cut yourself a slice.

Hamlins of Kensington

3 Abingdon Road, Kensington, London W8 6AH

Tel: 0171 376 2191 Fax: 0171 376 2191

Contact: Kelda Anderson. Last orders: 12 December. Switch, Delta, MasterCard, Visa, Amex. Personal shoppers only.

A most unusual Christmas-tree 'cake' costing £40 comes from Hamlins of Kensington, a small food shop just off Kensington High Street, using a really strong 70-per-cent cocoa solids chocolate. I will try and explain how it is made. The chocolate is hand-piped into 'twigs' radiating from a circle that are piled one on top of the other in ever decreasing circles, until the tree reaches about 12 inches and tapers to a point. Secured up the centre with a skewer, it does look like a miniature tree, and if you were feeling really inspired you could sprinkle icing sugar over it for snow. It may look rather amazing, but it is there to be eaten, so to munch your way through you simply break off a twig. Because of its fragility it cannot be sent by mail order, although Hamlins will deliver in London by arrangement.

John Pimblett & Sons Ltd

College Bakery, College Street, St Helens, Merseyside, WA10 1TP

Tel: 01744 28644 Fax: 01744 454027

Contact: John Pimblett. Last orders: 15 December. Switch, Delta, MasterCard, Visa. Delivery charge: £5.25 up to 5kg

John Pimblett & Sons are third-generation bakers based in and around St Helens in Lancashire. Launched last year was their mail-order range which, for a traditional family baker, contains a few surprises. Of course you will find the usual rich fruit cakes, either as plain, 'nut laden' or 'draped with soft sugar icing'. But it is for their appropriately named Christmas Jewel and Christmas Crown cakes that I single them out.

With glacé fruits and whole toasted brazil nuts heaped on top, the round Christmas Jewel is a relatively light cake made from unbleached wheat flour, butter, muscovado sugar and egg, with plenty of rum-soaked dried pineapple, apricots, figs and dates. A 1.2kg cake costs £23, and although there is little added sugar it is pleasantly sweet and generously fruity.

Based on an Italian recipe (although no one could actually tell me which one), the ring-shaped, hollowed centre Christmas Crown is exceptionally fruity. Its texture is less cake and more fruit slice. A mass of dates, cherries and various nuts are soaked in rum, with unbleached flour and eggs acting no more than as binding agents. Satisfyingly spiced, interestingly textured, the cake comes glazed with apricot jam and decorated with hazelnuts and almonds. It costs £19 for a 795g cake.

Meg Rivers Cakes

Middle Tysoe, Warwickshire, CV35 OSE

Tel: 01295 688101 Fax: 01295 680799

Contact: Meg Rivers. Last orders: 12 December. Switch, Delta, MasterCard, Visa. Delivery charge: £2.95 per delivery address.

What I have always liked about Meg Rivers' cakes is their wholesomeness. These are worthy cakes, made with organic flours and free-range eggs, and although it may seem like a contradiction in terms, the emphasis is on healthy eating. As Meg explains: 'Some of my cakes contain no added sugar; they don't need it as the natural sugars in the fruit make them sweet enough. Others have minimal or no added fat.'

The Christmas cake is generously packed with vine fruits, orange and lemon peel, walnuts and ground almonds. There is a pleasing hint of fieriness from added stem ginger, with a well judged spiciness, and it is sweet without cloying the palate and dense without being too heavy. Decorated on top with almonds, cherries and a sprig of holly (inedible), it is tied with a red and gold band around the cake and with red ribbon over the top. Prices range from £14.50 for a 1kg to £23.50 for a 2kg cake.

For several years Meg only ever sold plain cakes, but a couple of years ago she was forced to bow to pressure from her customers and start icing them. Now the same basic Christmas mix comes finished with a layer of almond paste and white fondant icing. You can choose from a poinsettia cake decorated with the flower in silk and tied up in a matching red ribbon trimmed in gold at £21.50 for a 1.2kg cake, or a maroon tartan cake with Happy Christmas stencilled in gold, a bunch of gold and maroon fruits (inedible) laid on top and a maroon and gold tartan bow, costing £32.50 for a 2kg cake.

Of course you could forget about a traditional Christmas cake altogether and plump for a cherry cake with the fruits soaked in kirsch, or a festival cake that contains a mixture of vine fruits, brazil and pecan nuts, pineapple, apricots, ginger and brandy, at £13.50 for a 1kg cake.

Mrs Gill's Country Cakes

Unit 5, Link House, Leat Street, Tiverton, Devon, EX16 5LG

Tel: 01884 242744 Fax: 01884 242744

Contact: Jacqueline Gill. Last orders: 5 December. No credit cards. Delivery charge: p&p extra.

Jacqueline Gill has long been a favourite cake-maker of mine. A born baker, she started a business baking to help out as her husband was a Lloyds casualty. The family's loss has proved our gain.

Using a rich dark fruit cake recipe 'from a friend in Canada, via Scotland', she has stuck with it ever since. She may have scaled up her through-put, but in essence hers is still a home-scale bakery. She still mixes in small batches, and will not compromise on the quality of the ingredients. The results are still as fresh and as polished as ever. Her cakes are very old-fashioned, rich and dark with just a hint of spice.

The ingredients are all of the best quality: equal quantities of plump currants, raisins and sultanas, juicy mixed peel, dark muscovado sugar, black treacle, unbleached white flour, butter, fresh eggs, fat glossy undyed black-red morello cherries, and brandy, whisky or sherry drizzled over the cakes as they come out of the oven. Matured for at least two months, Jacqueline's cakes are baked in 5, 6 and 7-inch rounds, either plain or generously decorated with neat circles of glistening cherries, walnuts and almonds. The Christmas cake uses the same mix but is then brushed with apricot glaze, covered with marzipan, iced and decorated with suitable seasonable cones and baubles, starting at £6.50 for a 5-inch cake.

The Priory Farm Shop

Priory Farm, Wrabness, Manningtree, Essex, CO11 2UG

Tel: 01255 880338

Contact: Clare Swift. Last orders: 20 November. No credit cards. Personal shoppers only.

At first glance the Priory Farm Shop looks like most other farm shops, with baskets of own-grown vegetables, jars of this and sacks of that. But look again, because tucked away stacked in the corner are Claire Swift's excellent fruit cakes. These are loose textured with a good crumb, generously endowed with fruit and noteworthy for what I can best describe as a honey aftertaste. But if you want to try Claire's cakes you will have to go there in person because, sad to say, this year they have stopped sending them out by mail order.

Following a recipe that has been in the family for years, Claire bakes in the farmhouse kitchen across the road from the shop. Production is small scale, running to no more than 'a couple of thousand a year', and she bakes three days a week in an exceptionally painstakingly way. There are two cakes: Traditional and Special. The Traditional's ingredients are Californian raisins, Australian sultanas and currants, unbleached self-raising white flour milled in Essex, unrefined demerara sugar, slightly salted butter, fresh eggs, mixed peel, glacé cherries, rum, and spices. For the Special, which is even richer and darker with a pronounced nuttiness, Claire substitutes muscovado for the demerara sugar, and adds chopped walnuts and 'a double dose of rum'. The rest of the ingredients remain the same.

Claire makes up batches of 4lb mixes in the morning. 'Larger than that would be difficult to handle. I cream using the mixer, but I stir the fruit in by hand as I think the machine crushes it. The bowls stand all day, and in the evening I tin up. I like to leave them standing, as it firms the mixture and gives the rum a chance to filter through.' Next comes the neat decoration on top of serried ranks of nuts, sorted by hand to make sure they match. 'And if you decorate before baking, it will stay perfect.' The cakes are left overnight, and the following day finished with an egg wash and baked.

The cakes are aged from two up to nine months. 'After that the top goes dull and the cakes seem to lose their glossiness.' They come in 2 and 4lb rounds and 4lb squares. There are also tin loaves. Prices start at £6.05 for an undecorated (plain) Traditional 2lb cake, up to £15.25 for a 4lb decorated Special.

The Village Bakery

Melmerby, Penrith, Cumbria, CA10 1HE

Tel: 01768 881515 Fax: 01768 881848 email: orders@village-bakery.com
Contact: Andrew Whitley. Last orders: 12 December. Switch, Delta, MasterCard, Visa, Diners. Delivery charge: £6 for orders under £20; £5 for £2–30; £4 for £30–60; over £60, carriage free.

When Andrew Whitley founded the Village Bakery over 20 years ago, his intention was to bake good products, using ecologically sound products working in an ecologically sound environment. Thus he uses only organic ingredients (to Soil Association standards) and his oven is wood fired. It burns compacted sawdust and genuine waste wood. Not only does this mean that Andrew is saving valuable resources but also, as he claims, 'it's twice as efficient as any good gas-fired or electric oven. Our oven's sole (brick floor) is heated by the fire to give a greater solidity of heat. It allows the heat to penetrate the bread so it bakes more evenly and faster, with a greater moisture retention – so you get a satisfying crust.'

The fruit cakes are baked in closed 'coffins' in the oven for a mere 1½ hours. 'The temperature is high for a cake, but they are well protected and baking them this fast means they don't loose much moisture.' Wheat free, sweetened without sugar and 100 per cent organic, they contain rye flour, barley and rice malt syrups, sultanas, raisins, apricots, dates, orange and lemon peel, eggs, with sunflower oil and bicarbonate of soda. Indeed they are very moist and very fruity, if a little on the heavy side. Sold in sizes of 1lb at £4.20, 2lb at £7.35 and 3lb at £9.99, these come plain and unadorned. However, new this year is Britain's only fully organic iced cake. The same cake is covered with a layer of organic marzipan (own made with ground almonds, eggs and sugar) and then covered in a layer of icing made from organic icing sugar. This iced cake is so new that I have neither seen a sample nor had details of the weight or price.

For Christmas, Andrew also bakes an organic lidded mince pie which cuts into 8 portions and costs £3.69. The pastry, made from 85-percent organic flour, sugar and margarine, is crisp and provides a good contrast with the own-made mincemeat mixed from apples, raisins, sultanas, cider vinegar, sunflower oil, sugar and spices that Andrew describes, rather unenticingly, as 'fruity gunge'. Should you prefer to make your own pies, you can buy 300g jars of the mincemeat for £3.25.

Short on equipment for icing and decorating the Christmas cake? Squire's Kitchen, 3 Waverley Lane, Farnham, Surrey, GU9 8BB (Tel: 01252 711749, Fax: 01252 714714) can supply everything you could possibly need, from crimpers and cutters to italic nib icing pens and silver or gold leaf.

Women's Institute markets are known for their excellent baked goodies. If you do not know where your nearest W I market is, you can obtain the list by sending £2 to WI Country Markets, Read Court, Rachel Road, Reading RG1 1NY (please make the cheque payable to WI Country Markets). Coming up to Christmas, they are certainly worth a trawl. You are bound to find tree decorations, Christmas puddings, mince pies, and some will even have poultry. Most branches will have their own Christmas fairs, and details of these are usually given in the local press.

Sweets and Chocolates

The Chocolate Society

Claypit Lane, Roecliffe, Borough Bridge, Yorkshire, YO5 9LS

Tel: 01423 322230 Fax: 01423 322253

Contact: Nicola Porter. Switch, Delta, MasterCard, Visa. Last orders: 17 December. Delivery charge: £2.50 for up to 1kg: £5 for any weight over 1kg.

Last year the Chocolate Society opened its first shop at 36 Elizabeth Street, London SW1W 9NZ (Tel: 0171 259 9222). If you have the chance, do pop in as there is masses to tempt you. Otherwise you are best off ordering direct from the Society's home base in Yorkshire.

Aficionados will probably be familiar already with the Society's cocoa pod 100g bars – the chocolate world's equivalent of single-estate extra-virgin olive oil. Each bar has a well-defined and different character. No 1 from Criolla beans is intense, clear and bitter-sweet, with an intriguing fruity flavour that reminds me of redcurrants. No 2, a mixture of various rare beans, is the strongest and most intense of the three, with a smoky after-taste. And No 3, from the Trinitario bean, is heady with a deep black finish. The percentage of cocoa solids ranges from 64 per cent (for No 1), 70 per cent (for No 2) and 66 per cent (for No 3); and the prices are £2.89 each.

With everything made using Valrohna chocolate, the Society's products can be relied on for plenty of chocolate 'punch'. New this year are the candied fruits, sold in 100g to 140g packs (depending on which fruit you choose). They are unusual not only for the selection of the fruit but also for the way different chocolate beans have been used to complement the fruits themselves. Strips of chewy candied orange are matched with the Trinitario bean, grapefruit goes with Guanaja, and a sharp lemon blends with an intense Manjari. Plump flame raisins from Chile are individually panned (dipped) in a lighter chocolate, and a plain chocolate bar comes studded with stem ginger.

There are plenty of novelties – snowmen, Christmas trees and so on – made with milk chocolate 'to appeal to the kids'. More sophisticated tastes will go for their fresh square chocolate truffles made from a *ganache* of fresh double cream, unsalted butter and chocolate, which come either plain or flavoured with a choice of fresh fruit purées such as raspberry, or liqueur such as champagne. Then there are the loose selections with some excellent pralines that are intensely nutty. These can be boxed to order. This year they are importing from Valrohna one foot square or round made-up chocolate boxes that will hold around 100 chocolates and cost about £50. That is a lot of chocolates to munch through over the holidays.

James Chocolates

Lower Westcombe Farm, Shepton Mallet, Somerset, BA4 6ER
Tel: 01749 8131300 Fax: 01749 831233
Contact: James Hutchins. Last orders: 14 December. Delivery charge: p&p extra.

James Hutchins of James Chocolates set up his business only in 1995. Currently on the move (he is temporarily working in the Bay Tree Food Company's old kitchen – see page 64), he hopes to be installed in a purpose-built unit by October, builders willing. I pass on this information merely so that you should know the trials and tribulations of any new food business. Not that he is unreliable or unable to fulfil his orders: far from it. But you might have to bear with him and the (minor) difficulties in speaking to him. Persevere, because it is worth it. James is good, and shows great flair and promise.

He is a self-taught chocolatier, and I am much impressed by the flavour and finish of his chocolates. Basically these can be divided into two kinds:- his pre-packed products and his loose chocolates. Dealing with the former first, these come wrapped in cellophane bags tied up with violet satin ribbon (my dog Violet approved), and cover such luscious treats as powerfully deep and dark Chocolate Lover Truffles. Made with a 70-per-cent cocoa solids chocolate and whipped fresh cream, and hand-rolled in cocoa powder, they cost £3.25 for a 100g bag (about seven truffles). The chocolate caramel nut crunch has the same intense hallmark. This time an own-made caramel is mixed with roasted hazelnuts, pecans and almonds, then dipped in chocolate. Sold in 125g bags costing £4.50, these are two-bite chocolates with a clever combination of textures and bitter-sweet tastes. I also loved his 'bars', more like knobbly logs, that come in three versions: white chocolate stuffed with apricot, almond and Amaretti; milk chocolate with sun-dried banana, cashew and caramel; and (best of all as far as I am concerned) dark chocolate with stem ginger.

James's style, he tells me, follows the French in that he hand-dips his chocolates rather than using moulded shells like the Belgians. His loose selection includes such gems as an intensely flavoured fresh raspberry, a fruity rhubarb and custard that is cunningly layered, and Amaretti Amaretto that has the crunchy biscuits on the outside and a *ganache* tinged with the liqueur inside. A boxed assortment will be available for Christmas.

The Old Smokehouse and Truffles

Brougham Hall, Brougham, Penrith, Cumbria, CA10 2DE

Tel: 01768 867772 Fax: 01768 867772

Contact: Rona Newsom. Last orders: 5 December. No credit cards. Delivery charge: prices include p&p.

The truffles from Brougham Hall are made with a good quality couverture, fresh cream, fresh compounds and real alcohol. And they have a freshness unsullied by the 'essences or flavouring' that mar so many of our British-made ones. With a choice of 16 fillings that include a strong, dark and sophisticatedly dry Coffee, Cointreau with a full fruitiness and strong alcoholic glow, black Russian (vodka and Tia Maria), caramel, ginger, and pear and brandy, they are piped or filled into round shells. Closed with a layer of couverture, the cases are rolled in yet more couverture and dusted in cocoa or sugar. A box of mixed truffles weighs either 200g at £8.50 or 300g at £14, and contains about 17 or 34 truffles respectively. Although selections are made up, no one seems to mind if you ask for your favourite fillings.

Plattinums

Buston Oast, Shingle Barn Lane, Hunton, Maidstone, Kent, ME15 0Q

Tel: 01622 820456 Fax: 01622 820457

Contact: Rory Clark. Last orders: 7 December. No credit cards. Delivery charge: 75p p&p for each box.

A Kentish cobnut is a cultivated type of hazelnut. A century ago, cobnut orchards or plats were a great feature of the Kentish countryside, extending over 7,000 acres. Now only 250 remain, centred on the stony soil of the parishes of Ightham, Plaxtol and Maidstone.

Rory Clark, with his 25 acres, is one of the largest growers. Until a couple of years ago he was content to send his crop to market. Then, with true entrepreneurial spirit, he started 'adding value' by developing a chocolate-coated cobnut. Such is his success that this year the entire 14-ton yield will be processed into his invention.

If you think that sounds an awful lot of chocolate cobnuts, in fact by the time the nuts have been prepared and are ready for their chocolate coating, the crop will only weigh a quarter of a ton. Apart from de-husking and shelling, the cobnuts' moisture content has to be reduced. 'When they are picked they contain something in the region of 43 to 50 per cent free moisture, but by the time I've finished with them it's less than 5 per cent,' Rory explained. Using maturer nuts picked in September through to October, for a better developed kernel and flavour, Rory first reduces their moisture by drying them in an oven set at a low heat which also hardens them, then roasts them at a higher temperature which also gives them a crunchy texture.

The final process of panning or coating in chocolate he leaves to the experts. The nuts are sent off to specialists (see below) who use a 57-per-cent cocoa-solid couverture. It is a skilled job, as the balance of chocolate to nut is all important. 'It's about equal weight of chocolate to nut. It has to be right as you want them neither too nutty nor too chocolatey.'

Packed in 125g boxes costing £5.95, containing around 50 nuts, these chocolate-coated nuts really are good. As you first sink your teeth into one you hit the plain chocolate. Keep going and you hit the crunch of the nut, making a pleasing combination of bitter sweet chocolate and rich, crisp nut. They really do make a very satisfying British-based chocolate, and all the better for using one of our truly regional specialities as their base.

La Praline Belge

26 Bankfield Drive, Shipley, Yorkshire, BD18 4AD

Tel: 01274 585281 Fax: 01274 826115

Contact: Peter Kyndt. Last orders: 12 December. Switch, Delta, MasterCard, Visa. Delivery charge: prices include p&p.

Guymarie Kyndt makes Belgian chocolates, but in Yorkshire. She trained at Callebaut College, attached to Callebaut's chocolate processing plant in Belgium, so it follows that she uses their couverture for her chocolates.

Belgian chocolates have a particular style. The *ganache* (centres) are soft, creamy in taste and texture (they are usually whipped), and poured into moulded cases or shells with a generous ratio of chocolate outers to filling. And true to her training and background, this is Guymarie's style. (Incidentally you may be interested to know that praline has become the generic word for all chocolates, rather like all vacuum cleaners are called hoovers.)

Made with fresh cream, unsalted butter and high strength alcohols as flavourings, her chocolates are rich, smooth and relatively sweet, with a great precision about their finish. They are sold in boxes tied up in a bow. A 200g assortment costs £7.15, 400g are £14. 25, and 800g are £28.50. With around 40 flavours ranging from cappuccino, a coffee cognac *ganache* in plain chocolate; Rembrandt, Cointreau flavoured sweet cream in milk chocolate; to Seville, a Grand Marnier *ganache* in white chocolate, the only problem is that the assortments come without a key, so it is rather difficult to tell which chocolate is which.

Rococo Chocolates

321 Kings Road, Chelsea, London SW3 5EP
Tel: 0171 352 5857 Fax: 0171 352 7360
email: venus@rococochocolates.demon.co.uk
Contact: Chantal Coady. Switch, Delta, MasterCard, Visa, Amex. Last orders: 15 December. Delivery charge: £2.05 for up to 300g; £3.40 for 300–750g; £4 for 750g–1kg; £4.70 for 1–1.25kg.

Rococo Chocolates sells interesting, good quality chocolates. Some are bought in but increasingly others are own-made in their dedicated chocolate factory. Particularly imaginative are the 70g Artisan bars costing £2.50 each. These are made with a deep dark chocolate with a 60-per-cent cocoa-solids content, infused with such 'wild' flavours as lavender, red chilli, cardamom, geranium, juniper or Earl Grey tea. Surprisingly pervasive but never over-poweringly so, the bars are also lifted by their texture. Minuscule amounts of the flavouring ingredient break up the smoothness to give them 'bite'.

For those who prefer their chocolate plain and simple, there are 85g House bars at £1.95 each in plain, milk, or white chocolate; sugar-free bars; and Valrhona Grand Cru bars from named cocoa beans: fruity Manjari from the Criollo bean and Guanaja or Caraibe, costing £3.25 for 85g. And there is a Rococo House bar including 100-per-cent cocoa solids.

Gift wrapped selections come in a choice of Traditional English, with such firm favourites as rose, or violet or strawberry cream, stem ginger and chocolate brazil; Fresh Cream truffles are flavoured with rum, Cointreau, malt whisky or champagne; and the Swiss collection has dipped apricot or pear, foiled noisette bars and escargot au lait (milk chocolate snails). These come made up into selections in a range of weights from 200g to 900g, with prices starting at £5.20 for the English, £7 for the truffles and £8 for the Swiss. Irresistibles would make good stocking fillers or for putting in bowls on the table and around the house. These include silver or gold leaf chocolate dragées at £3.50 for 100g, and a crate of twelve very realistic quails' eggs or green chocolate olives at £5.95 for 225g.

The pity is that most of Rococo's highly innovative and witty chocolate novelties cannot be sent by post as they are too fragile. This year they promise a foot-long pike filled with baby sardines, a World War II bomber plane flown by Father Christmas, and possibly a life-size salmon. If you have the chance, do drop in to see what else they have dreamed up.

Sara Jayne Truffles

517 Old York Road, Wandsworth, London SW18 1TF

Tel: 0181 874 8500 Fax: 0181 874 8575

Contact: Sara Jayne. Last orders: 10 December. No credit cards. charge: £4 p&p.

There are three secrets to a good truffle: the quality of the ingredients, the components of the *ganache* (centre), and the techniques used. Every chocolatier has his or her way of making a ganache. Some use butter and cream, some just butter, others eggs and cream, others eggs and butter and some even a mixture of all of the above.

Sara Jayne makes seriously good truffles. She uses just double cream with the chocolate. She can see no point in using any other fat as its flavour detracts from the purity and strength of the chocolate. For every pint of double cream, she uses two pounds of best, dark bitter couverture with a high content of cocoa solids. The cream is boiled, the chocolate broken up in pieces, added and generally fussed and stirred over until it is melted. Then it is left to cool and briefly whisked for lightness. Next come the flavourings, and I have seen Sara pour into the *ganache* literally cupfuls of Fine de Champagne or calvados or brandy (apparently a rough brandy works better than a smooth old cognac). These are the 'real thing', and there is no stinting with them here.

Then they are either rolled out by hand or piped for Venus nipples (Tia Maria enrobed in white chocolate). Some are rolled in cocoa powder or chopped nuts, others hand dipped into yet more chocolate to give them a glossy hard coat and a delightful contrast of textures: the hard chocolate cracks as you bite into the truffle, giving way to a rich soft yielding centre. Like Sara's nature (but not, I should add, her figure), the truffles are generous in every way, lavish in size – these are at least three-bite chocolates – and lavishly rich and creamy. A 1lb assortment box contains around 40 chocolates and costs £20, and they are also available in ½lb boxes at £12.

Sara also makes a butter-rich, crunchy – but definitely not grainy – fudge with butter, cream and sugar. Made in the old-fashioned way by boiling it up in an open pan, whisking it and then cooling it off, hers hints of a honeyed sweetness and comes in ½ and 1lb boxes costing £7 per pound.

The Toffee Shop

7 Brunswick Road, Penrith, Cumbria, CA11 7LU
Tel: 01768 862008 Fax: 01768 062008

Contact: Neil Boustead. Last orders: 10 November. Delivery charge: prices include p&p.

The Toffee Shop carries on its great tradition of making the best fudge and toffee in Britain. Since my very first visit there, nothing much has changed but why should it? Particularly when they have been using the same recipe to great effect for the last 90-odd years.

The fudge is simply glorious. Sold in oblong slabs, it is soft enough to break up with your hands into bite-size pieces. Take a bite through its velvet texture with the merest hint of grain and then wait – its clarity of rich butteriness explodes in your mouth. It is the purity of the ingredients that makes the fudge superb. Too many producers add glucose or glycerine or cheap flavourings, or substitute margarine for butter: additions that cloy the palate or make the fudge sickly sweet.

The Toffee Shop makes its fudge with butter, sugar and milk and nothing else. It is headet in pan-size batches to make sure it cooks evenly and does not catch, and it is stirred and fussed over as any good product should be. It comes plain – my favourite as it allows the full glory to shine through – and in two flavours: mint, using the same mint oil as in Kendal mint cake; and chocolate, using a dark plain chocolate. A word of warning: do not ask for a mixed box of fudge that includes mint. Neil Boustead will just not send it, because of the danger that the mint will overpower the other flavours.

The toffee is of an equally high standard. Made with butter, sugar and (this time) black treacle, it is set in tray and broken with a small hammer. The irregularly sized pieces are then wrapped by hand into paper twisted at the ends. Soft and chewy, with an amazing ability to seep through your teeth, the toffee is lushly buttery with the sweetness cut by dark treacle and a hint of spice. You will soon discover one is just not enough. Both fudge and toffee come in ½lb, 1lb, 1½lb, 2lb and 3lb boxes, and cost £3.45, £6.35, £9.86, £12.20, and £16.90 respectively.

Drinks of All Kinds

Christmas, we all agree, is the one time of the year when we can indulge ourselves. So having suggested what we might want to eat, let's turn in this section to what we might drink. In conjunction with Margaret Hickey, Food and Drink Editor of Country Living, I look at the range of seasonal drinks.

Choosing a particular wine to go with the meal strikes me as a thankless task. After all, you might prefer a Bordeaux to a Rhône, strike out for New World wines or decide to stick with champagne with every course. We have not, therefore, taken the liberty of telling you what you should drink, rather where you might buy it.

You can pick up some amazing wines at the supermarkets and the high street chains such as Oddbins, Majestic Wine Warehouses (who deal in cases only), Victoria Wine and the Thresher chain that encompasses Thresher Wine Shop, Bottoms Up and Wine Rack. With a free-ranging wine selection that is particularly strong on South African and New Zealand wines, Wine Rack - with the other stores in the Thresher group - also runs 'Drinks Direct', a home delivery and gift service. If you ring 0800 232221, you can not only order from their entire range of drinks but also get some very useful advice.

We have also selected the top ten independent wine merchants. These are chosen both for their range of wines and for the service they offer. Some specialise in particular areas, others run wide lists, but all are able to buy from the smaller vineyards which so often get overlooked by the large retailers. They print catalogues (some with highly informative wine notes), offer home delivery, are generally helpful and more than willing to make suggestions and guide you to the best within your budget. In general, they offer a service that wine buffs and novices alike value. And if you still feel the need for specific recommendations or bargains, we suggest you scan the columns of the newspaper and magazine wine writers.

Margaret and I have also listed our top ten champagnes, whiskies, liqueurs, and puddings wines. What's more, with the help of Adrian Bridge we have included a breakdown on port styles to ensure you know how to choose the right one. Our selection of drinks appeals to all tastes and pockets, and we hope you find at least one bottle here to give you, your family and friends great pleasure over the holidays. But, whatever you do, please take care and do not drink and drive.

Top ten wine merchants

Adnam's Wine Merchants

The Crown, High Street, Southwold, Suffolk, IP18 6DP

Tel: 01502 727220 Fax: 01502 727223 email: wines@adnams.co.uk

Contact: Robert Chase. MasterCard, Visa. Last orders: 15 December.

Delivery charge: orders over £100, carriage free; below that, £5.

Top of the list, and not just alphabetically, is Adnam's Wine Merchants. It has won the Wine Merchant of the Year award more times than I can remember. Dashing Simon Loftus (how many company chairmen do you know who sport a discreet gold earring?) and his team of buyers travel the world searching out the most impressive wines, and we, the wine-buying public, reap the benefits. They are not afraid to champion an unusual wine, such as Recioto Spumante, which they describe as 'frothy, papal-purple, rich fruit, bittersweet. Unique variant on the Recioto tradition. Goes well with glazed pear tart.'

Adnam's is based in Southwold, on the Suffolk coast, and the town is a charming seaside resort of the old-fashioned, beach-hut-on-the-shingle kind. You can buy from the shop, drink Adnam's beers in the pubs and stay in one of the Adnam's hotels if you are so inclined, but their mainstay for the wines is the mail order set-up. The half-yearly wine list is a pleasure to read, with its extremely eclectic range of wines and the quirky observations of its writers. It is also frank: Simon Loftus writes that his heart sank at an invitation to go to Canada on a wine-sampling trip because: 'previous experiences of Canadian wine had included formulaic international Chardonnays (the right amount of oak, the right amount of fruit, no soul) and weedy reds'. Instead, he finds to his delight elegant Pinots, fascinating Merlots and 'the finest cassis in the world' (see Top Ten Liqueurs, page 110). Prices range from £3.50 to £79 or so in the main catalogue; much more in the fine and rare wine supplement.

Avery's

Avery's Wine Cellars, 9 Culver Street, Bristol, BS1 5JE

Tel: 0117 921 4146 Fax: 0117 921 4146

Contact: Reinhard Jaechisch. Last orders: 5 December. Switch, Delta, MasterCard, Visa, Diners. Delivery charge: one case, £5.50; two or more cases, free.

Avery's has a big list of over 1,000 wines. The expertise of this wine merchant has been built up over nearly two centuries, so it would be fair to class them as a most traditional establishment. Sometimes this is not totally desirable. You long for a touch of excitement and fresh ideas about certain areas, such as the burgundy selection or the wines of Italy. But it has a good rapport with German wines and its understanding of

Spanish wines (particularly Riojas and the newer wines from Ribera del Duero and Somontano) is welcome. It also has a large choice of New World wines, notably from Australia, South America and South Africa, although again it could take a fresh look at some of the wines listed.

If you appreciate their commitment to quality, you might consider joining the Avery's Bin Club. You will be expected to invest around £30 minimum on a monthly basis, but there is no joining fee. From then on, you will be entitled to a 10 per cent discount on all wines printed in bold type on the list.

Bibendum Wine Ltd

113 Regent's Park Road, London NW1 8UR

Tel: 0171 916 7706 Fax: 0171 916 7705

email: sales@bibendum-wine.co.uk

Contact: Stephen Harrison. Switch, Delta, MasterCard, Visa, Amex. Delivery charge: free on 12 bottles or more.

Bibendum Wine is a lively, comparatively young (seven years old) company. It gets some of its character from globe-trotting Simon Farr, who scours the vineyards of the world (what a tough job) for interesting, affordable wines to put in their stylish list. It is not that Bibendum does not have wines at the upper end of the market, just the opposite, but you have to look at their fine-wine supplement for these. Worth checking out are the high-quality new names from Southern France, Burgundy, California and Italy, such as Calera (£11 to £25 a bottle) and Chalone Group (£9 to £28). If you can turn up for them, there are informal tastings on Friday evenings and Saturday lunchtimes, as well as organised vertical and horizontal tastings of high-grade clarets.

James Nicholson

27a Killyleagh Street, Crossgar, Co Down, BT30 9DG

Tel: 01396 830091 Fax: 01396 830028

Contact: Mark Jefferson. Switch, MasterCard, Visa. Last orders: 12 December. Delivery charge: p&p extra.

James Nicholson regularly wins hands down as the best wine merchant in Northern Ireland. He could give the merchants in the Republic a run for their money, too. The shop is a pleasure to wander around, but the list is where you see his full stock.

It is not absolutely comprehensive in all areas, but that is because he would rather not have a wine from a certain region than list an indifferent wine just for the sake of it. He needs to concentrate on gaps in his Spanish and South African coverage, but he has some first-class German wines, interesting Italian reds and a good selection of wines from all parts of France, notably Burgundy (Drouhin and Chopin-Groffier), Loire whites (Huet and André Dezat) and Rhône reds from Jaboulet Ainé and René Rostaing. He also keeps customers busy with a full calendar of tastings, tutored events and dinners, apart from regular newsletters listing new arrivals.

Justerini and Brooks

61 St James's Street, London SW1A 1LZ

Tel: 0171 493 8721 Fax: 0171 499 4653

Contact: Simon Walker. Switch, Delta, MasterCard, Visa, Amex, Diners. Last orders: 19 December. Delivery charge: under two cases £9; otherwise carriage free.

A posh wine merchants, Justerini and Brooks has a magnificent range: both deep and wide. Their huge Bordeaux section is awesome and top rate; they have an exciting range of burgundies; over 100 Rhône reds and a superb German selection. Their shops are in St James's Street, London (see above) and at 45 George Street, Edinburgh EH2 2HT (Tel: 0131 226 4202); but as the stock is so vast you cannot expect to see everything on the shelves at one time. But they will get things for you very quickly, if you are not too intimidated to ask.

Because Justerini and Brooks is so grand you will not find too many bargain-price bottles, but persevere as there are several good wines for under £10, and the bin-end sales throw up some bargains. Sarcey, their own-label champagne, is also worth investigating.

Lay and Wheeler

The Wine Market, Gosbeck's Park, Colchester, Essex, CO2 9TJ

Tel: 01206 764446: Fax: 01206 560002

home page: www.layandwheeler.co.uk

Contact: Richard Wheeler. Last orders: 18 December. Switch, Delta, MasterCard, Visa, Amex. Delivery charge: £5.95 on orders of less than £150.

If you are looking for a good knowledge of French, German and Australian wines, you are in good hands with Lay and Wheeler. The ethos of this family-owned firm of wine merchants is friendliness and reliability, with Richard Wheeler keeping an eye on it all.

The list is well represented in almost all areas, with strengths in France perhaps, but good coverage of elsewhere in Europe: Italy (they stock Angelo Gaja's Piedmont wines, as well as winners from Tuscany), Austria (Heinrich and Feiler-Artinger) and some classic Mosel Rieslings (Egon Muller, Fritz Haag and von Schubert) from Germany. Interesting choices from South Africa, Australia, New Zealand are all present, and from California they have selected some gems such as Peter Michael, Diamond Creek and the mighty Napa Duckhorn. Throughout the year, there are workshops for those keen to expand their palates, ranging from tastings to full-scale dinners with speakers.

Lea and Sandeman

301 Fulham Road, London SW10 9QH

Tel: 0171 376 4767 Fax: 0171 351 0275

Contact: Patrick Sandeman. Switch, Delta, MasterCard, Visa, Amex. Last orders: 19 December. Delivery charge: Over £150, free.

Charles Lea and Patrick Sandeman of Lea and Sandeman have established a good name for themselves in a short time. With three shops in London (the other two are at Barnes and Kensington Church Street), with in-store tastings every Saturday, the bulk of their business, however, is mail order. They are specialists in the wines of France and Italy, with Burgundy being their strongest suit. They say of their Burgundy list: 'This is one which has taken ten years to put together, since buying wine from Burgundy is a long-term commitment.'

They are a little snooty about the wines of the New World, especially Australia, and while their prices are not the keenest in the business, they have a very engaging enthusiasm, and are able to take on parcels of good wine that are too small for the larger players. Recently they brought over some Tuscan wines that had not been seen in this country previously (look for Tenuta del Terriccio, Le Machiole and Querciabella), and they have espoused the Loire, championing both the whites and the reds.

From their Burgundy list, I picked out the Saint Veran Domaine Daniel Barraud 1995, at £8.52, as being good value at the cheaper end of the scale, and Meursault Premier Cru Genevrières Domaine Charles et Remi Jobard 1994, at £23.95. If you have the money and the cellar, the Charmes Chambertin Grand Cru Domaine Bernard Dugat-Py 1994 at £45 promises to be superb in ten to twelve years.

Tanner's

26 Wyle Cop, Shrewsbury, Shrophsire, SY1 1XD

Tel: 01743 232400 Fax: 01743 344401 email: sales@tanners-wines.co.uk

Contact: John Melhuish. Switch, Delta, MasterCard, Visa, Amex. Last orders: 19 December. Delivery charge: over £75, carriage free; less than £75, £6.

Tanner's, a family-run wine merchants based in Shrewsbury, does rather tend to hide its light under the proverbial bushel. Its newsletter (the public face of the firm for most of its customers) is a little dull on the outside, but it contains great golden nuggets for those who care to look for them and its descriptions of the wines on offer are never less than honest. You will not find any dubious or gimmicky wines in Tanner's list because they are invariably well researched, and their prices are very keen too. One of their New Year resolutions, they write, is to 'scour our list for some of the very best value wines we can find and, for around a fiver a bottle, offer a mixed dozen in every edition'.

Tradition works hand in hand with a cautious innovation;

adventurousness, even. Look to them for special knowledge of France and Germany, although they have brought in some very good New World wines over recent years. Especially recommended are their Languedoc wines, although they are also strong in the Loire, Rhône reds and Michel Prunier, Henri Germain and Etienne Sauzet burgundies. You can find Tokaji from the Royal Tokaji Company, and the Alsace list is excellent: Rolly-Gassman, Hugel and Schlumberger. There are well-chosen New World wines, too, from New Zealand (Hunter's and Babich), Australia (Rockford) and South Africa (Hamilton-Russell), as well as a large selection of fine clarets and Sauternes.

The Wine Society

Gunnels Wood Road, Stevenage, Hertfordshire, SG1 2BG

Tel: 01438 741177 Fax: 01438 761167 email: winesociety@dial.pipex.com

Contact: Cathy Thomas. MasterCard, Visa. Last orders: 13 December.

Delivery charge: carriage free for a full case or orders over £75.

The Wine Society is not a wine merchant but, as its name suggests, a club. You can join for £20 and it entitles you to all the lists and newsletters.

The society has a number of showrooms, including one on the other side of the Channel, at Hesdin, not far from Boulogne and Calais, and this will give you the idea that the lists are strong on French wines. But German, Australian, Californian, New Zealand and South African wines are also well represented. If you do not know anyone to propose you, ring to see if they can arrange something anyway.

Yapp Brothers Ltd

The Old Brewery, Mere, Wiltshire, BA12 6DY

Tel: 01747 860423 Fax: 01747 860929

Contact: Robin Yapp. Switch, MasterCard, Visa. Last orders: 19 December.

Delivery charge: one case, £5; over two cases, free.

Robin Yapp has been importing wines from Provence, the Loire and the Rhône for more than 27 years, having left behind his dentist's drill and gone drilling for wine instead. His great coup was to have got in there early and discovered some of the great names in the business before they were more widely known. Even though the likes of Domaine de Trevallon were subsequently picked up and praised to the skies by the wine guru Robert Parker, you can still rely on supplies from Robin.

Do not look for wines outside his chosen areas, but do expect the selection within his fairly narrow frame to be the goods. And expect to enjoy his idiosyncratic notes in the list, which is illustrated with especially commissioned cartoons every year. Particularly tempting are Château Grillet and other northern Rhone whites, reds from Clape, Graillot and Chave, and Loire reds from Filliatreau and Druet.

Top ten champagnes

Alfred Gratien

This has been a champagne much admired by the insiders of the wine world, and it is just beginning to become more widely available in the UK (Oddbins Fine Wines, Sainsbury's, Fortnum & Mason and the Wine Society). It is an endearing champagne house, with no flash but masses of integrity, its rather basic offices offering a complete contrast with some of the palaces occupied by the grander houses. It produces, however, a most distinctive and distinguished champagne. Made in the old-fashioned way, with all the wines fermented in the cask, Alfred Gratien Champagnes are given plenty of bottle ageing before release. You should find a fresh bready/yeasty nose on the non-vintage Alfred Gratien Brut NV, and a creamy style at around £19.99. And if you're really ready to push the boat out to £45, Alfred Gratien Brut 1985 is a gorgeous wine, with its greeny-gold colour, its confident aromas of fresh bread and dark berry fruits, and flavour that is delicate yet full and long on the finish.

Billecart-Salmon

François Roland-Billecart is the mastermind of this very well respected house, and his policy is to build up the business slowly but very surely. It's hard to find anyone prepared to say a bad word about him or his wine, and this champagne is consistently sought out by critics and buyers. The Brut Rosé, in its squat, dark bottle, is particularly fine. Its colour (brought about by adding a small amount of red Champagne wine) is appropriately salmon and it has what Serena Sutcliffe calls a 'dancing elegance and finesse'. All the wines have exceptional ageing potential, and the vintage wines are particularly fine, being both robust and yet lively, and can be chosen to accompany even the main course of a meal. If you'd like to choose a vintage, then the Cuvée N-F Billecart Brut 1989 would be my recommendation. Billecart-Salmon Brut Rosé costs around £26.99, and the Cuvée N-F Billecart 1989 around £30.

Bollinger

This is an enduring favourite in the UK. Its style is full, with a (digestive) biscuity nose and good length, with the flavour going on and on. When you see RD on the label, it means that the wine has recently been disgorged and bottled, and this house is one of the very few that ferments its wines in oak. What's more, they keep their reserve wines in magnums (double the normal bottle size), an expensive, labour-intensive process that the house insists on, nevertheless, to maintain the unique house style. The winemaker believes the wine needs to spend time on the lees to enhance its character, and even the non-vintage has a minimum of three years aging before it is bottled. (The law insists on 12 months only.) The Grande Année is a fine instance of the top of the range, and the 1989 can be drunk well into the new millennium. Bollinger champagnes are especially good with food.

Bollinger Special Cuvée, widely available, costs around £24.99; the Grande Année 1989 costs around £38.99, from Harrods, Fortnum & Mason, Majestic Wines, Thresher, Victoria Wine and many top independent wine merchants.

Cuvée Napa

This is not a champagne as such, but it is made by the California house established by Mumm Champagne in what is often said to be the greatest wine-making valley, the Napa. The Mumm Cuvée Napa Vintage 1991 Brut is creamy and full-bodied, while the really exciting wine is the Blanc de Blancs, containing a touch of the Pinot Gris grape along with the Chardonnay, to give it a greeny-yellowy colour. It costs £11.99 from Oddbins and other good wine merchants.

Krug

The ultimate in expensive Champagnes, Krug has occasionally been accused of trading on its reputation, but it is the only house which vinifies all its wines in small oak *barriques*, and the extra care (and expense) that this entails really shows in the glass. The house style is uniquely vinous, with a full, rich, nutty signature, and the blending is brought to a fine art here, with 'up to 40 or 50 wines from 25 different growths and 6 to 10 different vintages', according to Henri Krug, winemaker. Around 80 per cent of production goes into making the Grande Cuvée, and its richnesss and depth is witness to the extraordinary feat of blending and it sells for around £70. The prestige wine of this prestige label is Krug Clos du Mesnil, produced solely from *grand cru* Chardonnay grapes in a walled vineyard in the greatest white wine village of the Côte des Blancs with the '85 the current vintage costing around £170 a bottle. The wine is so acid in its early years, it has the same effect as sucking a lemon, but given 15 years or so in the bottle it becomes magnificently profound. The 1982 is a particularly fine vintage.

Laurent Perrier

Laurent Perrier, a *grande marque* house 'probably produces the most varied and imaginative range of wines in the whole region', according to champagne expert Michael Edwards. Laurent Perrier Rosé NV (the biggest-selling rosé champagne not just in the UK but in the world) is made not by the more common practice of adding a little red wine to the white, but by the trickier method of putting the skins of the black Pinot Noir grapes into contact with the juice until some of their colour leaches out. It has instant appeal, being mellow and rounded yet with good acidity, and is often the best choice when you are uncertain whether a white wine will be robust enough.

The latest brainchild from their winemaker, *chef de cuvée* Alain Terrier, is Ultra Brut, a champagne that is uniquely without the sweet dosage (sometimes called *liqueur d'expédition*) that is added before the final cork goes in, in order to impart a little roundness to the wine once the yeasts have converted all the natural sugars to alcohol. It is the ultimate for lovers of the very driest champagnes, yet it is not acid, because the grapes have been very carefully selected for maximum ripeness, and the ensemble is appealing and elegant; a marvellous pick-me-up after any injudicious behaviour the night before. At around £24.99, it could well become a cult champagne. Available by mail order from Selfridges and Lea & Sandeman (see page 102). You can also ring 01628 475404 for other stockists.

Möet and Chandon

The standard Brut Imperial, at around £19.99, is the biggest selling champagne in the world, but year after year it maintains a consistently high standard. It is not the most exciting champagne but it will never let you down. Because the house is so huge and has such international clout, it can pay for the very best technical advice, and it can buy the best grapes in a hotly contested marketplace.

If you are one of the lucky people to be extended the hospitality of Möet and Chandon, you'll be entertained in a palace with a sunken garden and an orangery, the Trianon, which was built to accommodate Napoleon's court on its way to and from the battlefields of eastern Europe.

Its boyish-looking winemaker, Richard Geoffroy, is brimming with enthusiasm and his exceptional talents as a winemaker have made his reign one of the most successful ever. Möet has expanded overseas, to California's Napa Valley, where they make Domaine Chandon, and to Australia, home of Green Point; and Geoffroy has clocked up many thousands of air miles crossing the globe to oversee these enterprises. If you're looking for a New World equivalent of champagne, you could try either of these wines.

But if you want the very best the house can offer, Dom Perignon, named after the blind monk who started it all, has been the most famous champagne in the USA since 1933, when it was launched at the end of the Prohibition era, and is greatly sought after. It has a highish percentage of Chardonnay with very ripe Pinot Noir from the firm's own vineyards, and is simply sumptuous. Remove the bronze foil, uncork that dumpy bottle with its heart-shaped label, and relish the heavenly scent of toast and freshly roasted coffee. It is a wine that is guaranteed to stay in the memory. Dom Perignon 1990 costs £61.49, from a surprisingly wide range of stockists, including Tesco and Sainsbury's, as well as high street off-licences such as Oddbins.

Pol Roger

Famously Winston Churchill's favourite champagne, Pol Roger has long since been a favourite with British champagne lovers. The house is still family run, and it is distinguished by an integrity and lack of flashiness that carries through to the wine. Today's style is elegant and full of finesse. One of the prestige champagnes is named Cuvée Sir Winston Churchill (around £64), and here the Chardonnay and Pinot Noir grapes have been blended to produce a nutty, slightly smoky, robust flavour that seems very suitable for the character of the man it is named for. Pol Roger Brut Sans Année, White Foil, its non-vintage label, is a classic assemblage of the three Champagne grapes (Pinot Noir, Pinot Meunier and Chardonnay) in more or less equal measure. It has a floral bouquet and an almost honeyed taste, and should cost around £21.

Roederer

While most houses buy in their grapes, Roederer is almost self-sufficient with its well-sited vineyards, and this gives it great confidence. The wines are matured in stainless steel, but the house keeps its reserve wines in oak barrels, and a good percentage of these (around 20 per cent) goes into the non-vintage blend, Brut Premier, to impart that characteristic honeyed vanilla taste.

Its prestige label Cristal is one of the most unmistakable wines in the world. Unlike every other champagne, it comes in a clear bottle, the inheritance of a request from Tsar Alexander II, who required this wine to be rich (to satisfy his sweet tooth) and wanted it presented in a lead crystal decanter for his exclusive use. A great deal of it is exported to the United States, where it is highly prized. Look for the Cristal Vintage Brut 1989. This would be a splendidly rich, aged wine to crack open for Christmas Day or to let in the New Year, but will also keep for another four or five years if you wish.

Louis Roederer Brut Premier is very widely available for around £23.50. The 1989 Cristal is also available in many outlets for around £89.

Veuve Clicquot

The story of how Veuve Clicquot came to be recognised the world over is a story that is not uncommon in Champagne. After the death of her husband, the *veuve* (widow) took over and made a huge success of running the business, and this house owns a beautiful estate with one of largest vineyards in Champagne. Because it uses its own grapes, it has more control over the end product. Its wines are made using stainless steel entirely, with no wood ageing, but it achieves a nose that brings to mind peaches, raisins and vanilla, followed by a lively, fruity flavour (due in part to dominance of the dark grapes Pinot Noir and Pinot Meunier), and yet a freshness and crispness.

Annette Duce, wine supremo at Fortnum & Mason, drew my attention to the Veuve Clicquot Rich. Wonderfully versatile, it is able to cope with both creamy and sweet foods as well as spicier, brasher dishes. She feels it could both 'top and tail the meal', and would certainly create a pleasing unity because you would not have to serve too many wines. Veuve Clicquot Rich Reserve costs £32.99 from Fortnum & Mason and other good wine merchants.

Top ten whiskies

The Balvenie

Owned by William Grant and Sons, the makers of Glenfiddich, this Dufftown whisky has its own maltings and supplies the malt for its big brother. It has a squared-off shape; and while it seems at first acquaintance a sweet malt, it develops into a richness and a length which has won it its devotees. Around £20.99 for the ten-year-old.

Bowmore

This distillery is situated on Islay, that magical west-coast island which is home to many fine malts. This is one of the finest. It is paler in colour than some, but it is outstandingly smooth and elegant, with the peatiness held in check. Queen Victoria liked this particular whisky and had supplies sent to her in Windsor Castle.

Bowmore is a great distillery to visit, and it is interesting to note that the hot water that is a by-product of the process is fed through to the public swimming pool. Get the measure of this whisky by going for Bowmore Darkest (£36), Cask Strength (£34), or one of the two specially packaged decanter bottles. Available from Fortnum & Mason, and most good wine merchants.

Bushmills

This is the only whisky which is a whiskey, by virtue of being Irish. From its small base in Northern Ireland (its heritage goes back to at least 1608), this whiskey's fame has travelled the world. It is triple distilled, as is the Irish practice, and is a single malt which is matured mainly in bourbon casks to produce the unique house style. There is a vanilla fragrance coming from the oak, and the overall taste is slightly sweet, malty and smooth. Black Bush is around £16.99, and Bushmills' ten-year-old malt is £20 75.

The Glenlivet

The name of the glen where this Speyside malt is made was long considered a guarantee of the quality of a Highland whisky, dating back to the days of King George IV, and before. It is a malt of complex character, with both light and heavy peated malt in its make-up, as well as hard and soft water used in the distilling. The resultant whisky is spicy and smoky, with evidence of sherry in its maturing. The 12-year-old is £19.99.

Highland Park

On a hill overlooking Kirkwall, in Orkney, the present distillery stands on the site of an illicit 18th-century still, and there is still an air of romance to the place. It has its own maltings (now very rare), although barley is imported from the mainland. Orkney peat helps to give it its distinct aroma, and a little heather is burnt in with it, which may also have its effect. The distinctively shaped bottle is a common sight after dinner, when real single malt connoisseurs gather. The 12-year-old is around £22.49.

Laphroaig

This is another Islay single malt and distillery, the very embodiment of what an Islay whisky is believed to be. It is uncompromisingly big and peaty, with plenty of aroma and a knock-out flavour. It will not be suitable for every occasion, being so very marked in its character, but it is a top choice for many when they want to savour its salty, smoky tang.

The Macallan

This has long been regarded as one of the finest Speyside malts. From its first (legal) days in 1824, its reputation spread quickly, and even though today its output is growing, it continues to use small stills and matures its spirit in sherry casks. (It is, by the way, a particularly attractive distillery to visit.) I find in it hints of fennel and spice; it is known for its smoothness and enjoys a long finish. Expect to pay around £22.49 for the ten-year-old, and £39.99 for the 18-year-old.

Old Fettercairn

This is a fine old Highland single malt, located on the Fasque estate, hard by William Gladstone's family house. The distillery is set in picturesque countryside, and the malt itself is lightly peated, but sufficiently balanced for the smoky, peaty flavour to come through alongside the spicy, nutty maltiness.

Springbank

From legendary Campbeltown, once the 'whisky capital' of Scotland, this family-run firm is unmistakable and idiosyncratic, from its quirky distillation process, which baffles even experienced observers, to its insistence on bottling the whisky on site. The Springbank malt is a fine dram, reminiscent of the attack of an Irish whiskey, with a touch of sweetness and a long finish. For the 21-year-old you will pay around £40.99.

Talisker

Robert Louis Stevenson described this as 'the king o' drinks' in a poem of 1880, and this full-bodied, smoky whisky is full of character in the way of the Islay malts, but with its own unique twist. This is the only distillery on the Isle of Skye, built in 1831 by two brothers who used to live in Talisker House, visited in former times by Boswell and Johnson and by Sir Walter Scott. The ten-year-old is around £24.99.

Top ten liqueurs

Benedictine

On the coast of Normandy, at Fécamp, there is a Benedictine abbey where in 1510 Don Bernardo Vincelli used to labour over an elixir designed to give his brothers vigour and vim, and to act as a shield against the ever-present plagues and epidemics of the day. The tradition continued until the time of the Revolution, but some 70 years later the recipe was rediscovered and the formula developed to make the liqueur we know today.

The exact ingredients are not revealed, but some 27 herbs and spices go into Benedictine, giving it a vegetal, piquant flavour, and its restorative powers are still trusted. The letters so prominent on the label, DOM, stand for Deo Optimo Maximo - to God, most good, most mighty.

Chartreuse

At any one time, only four or five people know the secret recipe for Chartreuse, both the green and the yellow varieties. And most of them are sworn to silence as this is the liqueur made by the contemplative order of the Carthusian monks near their monastery close by the French Alps. The brothers work in a modern distillery, but the recipe that dates from 1605 has scarcely changed since then. With its unique blend of 130 ingredients, the Green, which is herbal and minty in character, can be drunk over ice or poured into strong coffee, while the golden version is sweeter and may also be drunk very chilled or blended with the green. It is a noble potion, intensely strong (55 per cent vol) and some connoisseurs, such as wine writer Oz Clarke, rate it the finest of all liqueurs. Around £19.99.

Eau-de-Vie de Pommes – The Somerset Cider Brandy Company

First from cider-maker Julian Temperley came Somerset Royal Cider Brandy, England's answer to Calvados, and now he has produced a drink with the most intense apple aroma of any I know. Working down in Somerset, where he sets himself the highest standards, Julian has distilled Britain's first apple eau de vie, and it makes a fine sipping glass at the end of the meal. It costs £11.00 for a 37.5cl bottle, packaged in its own wooden box, and available from Fortnum & Mason and Lea & Sandeman.

Framboise – Wines of Canada

From Southbrook Farms, Canada, come the most spectacularly perfumed fruit essences: framboise and cassis. The cassis (blackcurrant) is luscious and heady, but for me the pure kick of raspberry in all its full fragrance and quintessential fruit is stunning. It can be served with white wine, or even, if you're feeling hedonistic, poured over vanilla or raspberry ice cream. Southbrook Farms' Canadian Framboise is available in 35cl botttles from Waitrose, Asda, Majestic and Harrods, priced at around £7.99. The Canadian Cassis is available from Asda and Majestic for around the same price.

Grand Marnier

This is the very essence of the orange. Taking a cognac spirit base aged in the Charente region of France, the makers' recipe has been developed from an 1870s original, which used bitter oranges imported from Haiti. The secret lies in macerating the orange peel in the cognac spirit and then re-distilling it, to stabilise the liquor. Then the distillate is further blended with cognac and sugar syrup, producing the Triple Orange Grand Marnier liqueur. It is so popular that a bottle is sold every few seconds somewhere in the world, and costs around £18.99.

Kummel

The first documented liqueur was a caraway preparation distilled just outside Amsterdam by Lucas Bols in 1575. The known digestive properties of caraway were called into play, as well as the flavour it imparted to the spirit, and it may be considered as the first digestif. It remains today a sophisticated and elegant after-dinner drink, translucent and perfumed, best drunk very chilled from shot glasses. The two labels to look for are Wolfschmidt (the UK label) and Mentzendorff, made in Saumur, France. Around £13.99 for a 50cl bottle.

L'Oro di Amalfi, Liquore di Limone

Italians are known for their love of the sun, sensual pleasure and the good things in life, and so it is appropriate that they have produced this liqueur (also called Limoncello) with its yellow hue and an aroma that calls to mind lemons warmed by Mediterranean sunshine. The bottle is tall with a long neck, and from it pours a liqueur that is warming and rich, yet with a hint of bitterness from the citrus fruit: lemons from Amalfi. Best served very well chilled, it is extraordinarily well suited to Christmas time as it gives a promise of sunny days to come. A bottle costs £18.50. Call 0171 259 5761 for details of stockists.

Poire Williams

This *eau-de-vie*, or fruit brandy, is the unsweetened distillate of ripe pears, and it is unspeakably delicious in its simplicity and purity. Colourless, dry and with a heavenly perfume, this is one of the greatest after-dinner drinks I know. You can also buy a bottle in which the fruit miraculously (it seems) appears whole, despite the narrow neck, proving that the ship in the bottle is not the only example of legerdemain. Vieille Prune (plum) from the same company is also excellent. Available from Fortnum & Mason and other good wine merchants for £11.49 for a 50cl bottle.

Porthallow

This is a good UK company that deserves applause for its commitment to quality. From Cornwall, where they knew a lot about spirits in the days of wreckers and runners, comes a wholly legitimate range of spirits, of which the most Christmassy are the Sloe Gin and the Ginger Whisky, two drinks designed to warm the cockles of your own and anybody else's heart. They are available from Fortnum & Mason, costing £11.95 each.

Southern Comfort

Possibly we all know this was Janis Joplin's favourite drink. And although the precise ingredients are not revealed, people frequently guess it to be a bourbon whisky base, with peach essence to give it its distinctive peachy flavour. It was first produced in New Orleans by a bartender who contrived to mask the flavour of some indifferent whisky by adding a few glugs of this and that of his own devising. He was so successful that he moved to Memphis, opening a bar on its famous Beale Street, and finally to Saint Louis. Its label proclaims it to be 'The Grand Old Drink of the South', and its fame has spread until it is the fourth biggest selling liqueur in the world, costing around £15.69 in this country.

Top ten pudding wines

Chateau Climens

An opulent wine, a little less well known than Yquem, this Sauternes-Barsac is elegant and finely balanced. Classically, it is made from the Semillon grape which has been allowed to develop 'noble rot'. It has the classic Sauternes style, with an identity of its own. Waitrose Direct (Tel: 0800 188881) have a 1991 version for £28.50, and it is also to be found at a host of good wine merchants.

Chateau d'Yquem

Quite simply one of the great wines of the world, and the epitome of fine Sauterne. Jancis Robinson, wine writer and broadcaster, says it's 'famous from Texas to Tokyo'. To the base grape, Semillon, which gives the wine its lusciousness, is added a percentage of the Sauvignon Blanc grape, which contributes acidity and aroma. After the wine has been bottled, it takes on colour and can deepen to a foxy, tawny tint. Simultaneously the wine loses its obvious sweetness and takes on complexity, to end up being rich, almost burnt in its first impressions and somewhat akin to butterscotch. You will also find, perhaps, honey, apricots and pineapple.

Deinhard Bernkasteler Doctor Trockenbeerenauslese

Wines from Germany are frequently cited by wine lovers when they are selecting their fantasy cellar, but too much indifferent semi-sweet pop has issued from Germany in the last few decades, and has given the whole country a bad name. At their best, the great German estate wines are finely structured, multi-layered in their complexity, and give lasting pleasure. One such is this highly perfumed wine that will create a good impression in any company. The Riesling grape is the one favoured in Germany, giving an enhanced perfume but a slightly more austere taste than the Semillon-based sweet wines. From Oddbins Fine Wines and other good wine merchants.

Duke of Clarence Malmsey – Blandy's

Madeira is quite simply one of the world's great wines. When Jancis Robinson was invited to make her selection for Desert Island Discs, she chose Madeira as her luxury, partly for the very sensible reason that this is the only wine that does not deteriorate once it has been opened. Oxidisation holds no fears for the Malmsey drinker! In fact, Madeira thrives on rough treatment, enjoying being baked, shaken and generally kicked around. The resultant wine is magnificent. Of the different styles of Madeira, Malmsey is the sweetest, and this example from the old family firm is both rich and seductive.

Founder Liqueur Muscat – Baileys of Glenrowan, Victoria, Australia

The climate and the exuberant fruit so characteristic of this part of Australia can be harnessed to make some of the most splendidly rich pudding wines. Founder Liqueur Muscat has a wonderful nose, and carries through in the glass to give a thoroughly satisfying wine at a fair price. Available from Oddbins.

Monbazillac Chateau Bellevue

Monbazillac is a region of France where the climate favours the growing of the Semillon grape, and at its best its wines can draw comparison with Sauternes; but this enclave of Bergerac is not as consistent as it might be. This château, however, can produce good results even in less favourable years.

Recioto della Valpolicella

This is Italy's answer to port. It is not a fortified wine, but it reaches higher levels of alcohol than average table wines because the grapes are allowed to dry and become more concentrated after harvesting and before fermentation and vinifying. The best examples of Recioto della Valpolicella show herby, bitter cherry and dark berry fruit flavours, and the intense purplish colour is appealing. From Adnam's.

Samos Nectar

Greece was once the very fount of wine, but its reputation is no longer what it was. This is sad, and memories of holiday retsina have clouded our vision of what this country can produce. From the island of Samos, on the eastern edges of the Greek archipelago, hard by the Turkish coast, comes this sensational sweet wine. It tastes of sun-baked apricots and honey, but the structure is such that it is not cloying. What is more, it comes at a bargain price and in a blind tasting could well pass for a wine more than twice the cost.

Szt Tamas Tokaji, 5 puttonyos 1991 Royal Tokaji Co

This marvellously honeyed wine from Hungary is one of the three First Growths, following the 1700 classification. It is golden and luscious and one of the great sweet wines of the world. Worth the £34.50 it will cost for a 50cl bottle. From Waitrose, among others. The budget version, Tokaji Aszu 5 Puttonyos 1988, is £9.99 for a 50cl bottle from Oddbins.

Valdespina Solera 1842 Oloroso Viejo Dulce

Spain is a country of widely varying climates, and its long tradition of fine wine-making is never exceeded when it comes to the making of sherry. The solera method of ageing sherry takes the wine through a succession of barrels, with younger wines being added to one barrel to refresh its contents as a percentage of the more mature wine is moved on to another barrel, and so on. This long, labour-intensive process results in a complex wine in which youth and maturity come to a point of equilibrium.

Port

Christmas and Port inevitably go together, for port is rich, warming, pleasurable and full of good cheer, a perfect symbol for Christmas.

Port wine comes from the Upper Douro valley region of northern Portugal, the oldest demarcated wine region in the world. It is made from different indigenous grape varieties grown in this area since Roman times. The grapes are harvested in late September and fermented in stainless steel vats. (Some companies still tread their grapes in lagares, traditional stone vats, for a greater intensity of fruit.) The essential method of making port, however, remains constant.

After half of the natural grape sugar has fermented into alcohol, the winemaker adds a natural grape spirit to 'fortify' the wine. What actually happens is that the fortification process raises the alcohol level to 20°, which kills off the yeasts and leaves a large amount of unfermented natural grape sugar. This is why port is sweet. The quality of the vineyards and grapes will determine how long the port is aged and how it is blended before sale.

Port shippers are the companies that age and blend their ports in Vila Nova de Gaia just across the river from Oporto. Many are household names and many continue to tend their own vineyards. Some are family companies still run by the descendants of the founders, with several maintaining strong British ties. Others are subsidiaries of multinational companies.

As Adrian Bridge of Taylor's Port points out, each shipper has its own house style and it is this (and the attention to quality) that gives each port its particular personality and character. Taylor's ports are considered classic and elegant, Fonseca's full, fruity and powerful. The ports from Graham's are intensely sweet, Cockburn's are drier, and Dow's big and tannic.

There are also a number of different styles of port, ranging from Ruby and Young Tawny to Classic Vintage reserved for the heights of celebration, with varying prices. To derive maximum satisfaction from your bottle of port, first you need to know which style you want to drink, then decide which port shipper provides the best example.

Ruby and Young Tawny

These are the 'basic' ports, which account for 80 per cent of all port production. Mostly sold on the Continent where they are drunk as an aperitif, in Britain they tend to be used primarily for cooking. What would our Cumberland sauce be like without a liberal dash of port? They are blends of young port that have been aged for about 2½ years in stainless steel. Plummy and sweet, they lack any real character, with the tawny showing lighter colour than the ruby. Prices start at about £5.49 and I suggest buying the own label wines from the supermarkets – Tesco and Sainsbury's have good examples - or Sandeman Ruby.

Vintage Character

Once called Premium Ruby, a Vintage Character port is a blend of wines from several years and aged for about four years. Displaying a greater depth of berry fruit flavour than a basic ruby, they have not yet acquired the complexity of some of the finer styles. But soft and smooth, these ports make for an 'easy' drink. A great favourite in Britain is Cockburn

Special Reserve, widely available at £7.99, or Fonseca's Bin 27. Initially reserved for the family members, this wine was commercialised in the early 1970s and is available from Victoria Wine and many independent specialists at £8.49. It is the only Vintage Character port that contains foot-trodden wines, and this shows in its extra intensity of ripe, jammy fruit.

Late Bottled Vintage – LBV

Very popular in Britain, this style was introduced by Taylor's Port in 1970 as an alternative to Vintage port. The wine is selected from a single harvest and aged in large oak vats. Unlike Vintage port which is aged in vats for only two years before bottling, LBV port is left in oak for five or six years before bottling. It is also filtered prior to bottling, so it does not throw a deposit or need decanting before drinking. And it also has the advantage that, once opened, it will last for three to four weeks without losing its full fruit.

Taylor's, the inventor of this style, still offers the best quality. Its Late Bottled Vintage port is spicy with hints of chocolate on the nose, yet full, fruity and complex in the mouth. Widely available from Threshers, Wine Rack, Waitrose and Sainsbury's, it costs £10.49. Croft's Late Bottled Vintage port is also spicy on the nose, with a plummy and fresh flavour, and costs £10.49 from Asda.

An alternative to Late Bottled Vintage is Traditional Late Bottled Vintage. Despite its name, this is a more recent style which started to appear in the late 1980s. It differs from LBV in that it is unfiltered, so the wines require decanting through a damp butter muslin prior to serving. A good example is Churchill Graham, costing £10.50 and available from Fortnum & Mason, The Wine Society and Booths.

Aged Tawny

Aged Tawny port should not be confused with young inexpensive Tawny port (see above) as there could not be a greater contrast. These are high-quality blended wines that have been matured in small oak casks and consequently have been exposed to a great deal of wood contact and evaporation. The wood contact 'bleaches' out the colour, while the evaporation concentrates the wine and produces wonderful raisiny, nutty flavours.

When buying, you will know if you have chosen an Aged Tawny by checking the label (it declares its age along the lines of 'Ten year-old'). These wines are rich yet complex, with wonderful long finishes. Try Taylor's 10-year-old from Fortnum & Mason and Harrods at £17.49. Noval produce tawny ports which are silky and raisiny with hints of toffee. A sampling pack of their full line up of 10-, 20-, 30- and 40-year-old is packed in a neat portable case and costs £24.99 from Threshers.

Single Quinta

Single Quinta ports are true Vintage ports but made in non-declared years (see below). Often referred to in the trade as non-classic Vintages, they are wines from a single year and a single vineyard that have matured in the bottle. They will need decanting and, like classic Vintage port, are best enjoyed within 48 hours of opening.

Considered wine for special Christmas drinking, they are generally far better value than their classic cousins. They tend to reach their peak at between 10 and 14 years after the harvest, but will continue to mature for longer. Worth drinking is Quinta de Vargellas 1984 (winner of the Wine Magazine Port Trophy in 1996), with its hint of violets in the aroma, that costs £18.99 from Lay & Wheeler, Thresher's and Victoria Wine. Or try Guimaraens 1982, with its plum fruit and spicy aromas and lingering finish, at £18.99 from Sainsbury's.

Vintage

The rarest and most expensive of all ports, they are only produced when the port shippers declare a vintage which, on average, is no more than three times a decade. Made from a single harvest, the natural sugars in the ripe grapes and the tannins and spicy notes all mature monumentally slowly in the bottle, after having spent two years in the oak casks.

You may well read about the relative merits of the 1927 Cockburn's compared with the 1945 Warre - the longest lasting of all ports - but few of us could afford to buy them. Even if we could, they are rare to find, although I believe both Avery's and the Wine Society (see pages 99 & 103) hold a few bottles). Of the more recent vintages, the 1970 is drinking very well, as are the 1980 and 1983. The 1977, however, should be laid aside until the turn of the century, and the 1985 (comparatively cheaply priced at around £30.00) will not be ready for drinking until a good ten years from now. If you want to give someone a really special Christmas present, give them a bottle of the recently declared 1994 vintage, which will set you back around £80.00. Then just hope that they ask you back in 20 years time to share it with you.

The days on either side of Christmas

Christmas Standbys

Cheese

Colston Bassett & District Dairy Ltd

Harby Lane, Colston Bassett, Nottinghamshire, NG12 3FN

Tel: 01949 81322 Fax: 01949 81132

Contact: Richard Rowlett. Last orders: 8 December. No credit cards. Delivery charge: p&p extra.

Stilton is inextricably linked to Christmas. Traditionalists insist on it over the holidays. Don't ask me why, but they think no other cheese will do. The Mitchell Beazley *Pocket Cheese Book* describes it as follows: 'velvety, close textured, unpressed with a pale ivory paste grading to amber at the edges and marbled with greenish-blue veins. The rind is dry, crusty, greyish brown and slightly wrinkled with white powdery patches. The flavour ranges from mild with a sharp edge when young, to rich and tangy when mature.'

You can buy Stilton from just about every supermarket, deli or cheese shop at this time of year (see also Neal's Yard, page 126). Some are good, others insipid, and on no account should you even think of buying it squashed into a jar. You might think it looks good and makes an ideal present, but the cheese is often second rate. Rumour has it that only poor quality cheeses are ever used.

When choosing a Stilton, always look for evenly distributed veins, a good bluing and a good contrast between the paste and veins. Although you may be tempted to buy a small truckle, it is not necessarily a good idea. Their flavour is not nearly so highly developed because, as they dry out far more quickly, they mature when far younger. Colston Bassett, a small farmers' co-operative dairy who make a Stilton of great creaminess and mellow fruitiness, do not even make them for this reason. They advise buying a piece off a large cheese, and sell whole, half, or quarter cheeses and a baby Stilton which weighs approximately 6lb.

As for the vexed question of how to cut into a round Stilton, scoops are thought a bad idea. Far better to cut it cross-wise with a knife, working your way through the cheese. Always keep your Stilton in a cool place, preferably a larder; if you do not have one, a fridge will do. Some people wrap it in a lightly moistened cloth to stop it from drying out, others use foil or cling wrap. And remember to unwrap and leave it at room temperature a good couple of hours before you want to eat it.

Peter Gott
Sillfield Farm, Endmoor, Kendal, Cumbria, LA8 0HZ
Tel: 01539 567609 Fax: 01539 567483
Contact: Peter Gott. Last orders: 12 December. No credit cards. Delivery charge: prices include p&p.

If you think Lancashire cheese has no more to offer than a sharp flavour and a dry crumbly texture, then think again. Made with two- and sometimes even three-day curds, proper Lancashire can be rich and buttery, with a honeyed, flower-fresh flavour.

When I judged the cheese classes at the Great Eccleston Show near Blackpool last year, there were some very fine cheeses. The problem is that you can hardly ever buy these Lancashires out of the county, partly because Lancastrians know a good thing and hang on to it and partly because it is so rich, buttery and crumbly that it almost impossible to pre-pack. If you buy your Lancashire from a supermarket, what you tend to find there are those acid cheeses that are no more than pale imitations of the real thing but are so much easier to cut and pack.

Mrs Kirkham's unpasteurised Lancashire may be familiar to anyone who haunts the cheese shops (see Neal's Yard Dairy, page 126), but there are others that are also worth seeking out. Luckily, Lancastrian Peter Gott will supply them, cut from a 42lb traditional cylinder, with a minimum order of one pound in weight. Carron Lodge (last year's winner of the traditional class) makes a buttery cheese with a reverberating light grassy sweetness, which Peter sells at around 11 weeks old costing £4.50 per pound. Sandhams, a creamy medium tasty cheese of between five and six months, 'promises well this year' and costs £4.80; and the unpasteurised Shorrocks, at four to five months, is a tangy cheese with plenty of 'smack' at £4.80 per pound. Peter also describes it as 'slightly drier and more acid but nonetheless with a smooth but open flavour with a wide avenue of taste'.

Baked Camembert

Choose a ripe but reasonably firm Camembert about 15cm (6in) in diameter. Finding a ripe one can be a bit of a problem, so it might be wise to buy it in advance and leave it to ripen. Using a sharp knife, slice the top off, then lay it back on top of the cheese. Bake in a preheated oven at 200°C/400°F/gas mark 6 for about 15 minutes. Remove the lid and arrange the cheese on a plate surrounded by crackers or mini oatcakes. Serve with drinks before a meal and let everyone dip into the cheese, which should be gloriously melted and runny.

Iain Mellis

30a Victoria Street, Edinburgh, EH1 2JW

Tel: 0131 226 6215

Contact: Iain Mellis. Last orders: 19 December. Switch, Delta, MasterCard, Visa. Delivery charge: £6.50 for up to 15kg anywhere in Scotland excluding Highlands and Islands; £8.50 for anywhere else.

Iain Mellis is one of the very few cheesemongers who really understands the nature of cheese. Fourteen years' experience in cheese-making has taught him that, if nothing else. And with two shops in Scotland (the other is at 492 Great Western Road, Glasgow, G12 8EW, Tel/Fax: 0141 339 8998), he concentrates on on-farm cheeses collected from all over Britain and Ireland. What also singles out his cheeses is their condition. Iain knows how to look after them, keeping them in his air-conditioned and humidity-controlled cellars. And he buys off the farm, ripening if necessary to peak condition.

Amongst the cheeses he recommends for Christmas are a Baby Dunsyre weighing around 1lb and costing £8.50. Iain describes it as 'gorgeously creamy, with a soft, long blue mellowness. Each flavour is distinct but perfectly poised before a stunningly long aftertaste. Memorable and sublime'. Then there is the Camembert-style Bonchester made in the Borders and matured on by Iain for at least six weeks to allow its full creaminess to develop; or a slice of Gowrie cut from a 60lb truckle for a buttery Cheddar-style cheese but with a softer texture.

Have you noticed how many good cheese shops there are now in Britain? Not enough perhaps, but still a lot more than a few years ago. Listed below are just a few of my other favourites who offer a mail order service:

Country Cheeses, Market Road, Tavistock, PL19 0BW (Tel: 01822 615035, Fax: 01837 840811) stocks only British cheeses. Based in the South West, they focus on that area so their cheeses predominantly come from Cornwall, Devon, Dorset, Somerset and just pushing into the edges of Avon. They offer cheese selections under such colourful titles as More Cheese Less Bored, or Billy's Bundle (goats' cheeses). The actual cheeses will vary, as they select according to what is best at that moment, so you need to ring to discuss any order. They are a small but very friendly and helpful shop.

Jeroboams, 96 Holland Park Avenue, W11 3RB (Tel: 0171 727 9359, Fax: 0171 792 3672) with a branch at 51 Elizabeth Street, Belgravia (see also page 162) is perhaps stronger on French than British cheeses, but they have a good selection of both. This year the French Farmhouse selection, costing £36.50, is made up of Camembert, Chaource, Pavé d'Affinois, Reblochonnet, Banon, Sancerre, Selles sur Cher and Bleu de Laqueuille. They also run a Cheese Club costing £22.50 a month that sends out inspiring choices with the odd unusual 'special'.

Paxton & Whitfield, 93 Jermyn Street, London SW1Y 6JE (Tel: 0171 930 0259, Fax: 0171 321 0621) have been cheesemongers since 1797. Surrounded by gentlemen's clubs and gentlemen's outfitters, they have a reputation for being conservative in their outlook, but in fact they have as good a selection as most of the newer on-farm British cheeses. They also stock whole hams, and at Christmas time you are bound to see gentlemen queueing up to collect their orders. They have started a Cheese Society and members receive a newsletter, special offers and invitations to cheese tastings.

A keen supporter of the small cheese-maker, Ann-Marie Down at **The Fine Cheese Co**, 29–31 Walcot Street, Bath, BA1 5BN (Tel/Fax: 01225 483407), with a branch at 5 Regent Street, Cheltenham, stocks around eighty British cheeses, most of them unpasteurised, and the equivalent number of foreign cheeses. For Christmas, they also sell cheese selections in stylish gift boxes, and a good selection of regional foods.

Montgomery's Cheddar
Manor Farm, North Cadbury, Yeovil, Somerset, BA22 7DW
Tel: 01963 440243 Fax: 01963 440243
Contact: James Montgomery. Last orders: 20 December. No credit cards.
Delivery charge: about £1.50 p&p.

As far as I know only two farms exclusively make an unpasteurised traditional farmhouse cheddar: here at North Cadbury, and at Moorhayes where the Keen family run their dairy. Most people believe, and rightly, that an unpasteurised cheese is more interesting and complex than a pasteurised one. As Randolph Hodgson of Neal's Yard Dairy (see page 126) aptly said, 'the difference is the same as listening to music in stereo or mono'. It is a constant source of surprise that people are worried about the health risks of unpasteurised cheese. If the milk is carefully handled and regularly tested, and scrupulous hygiene is practised, there should be no danger.

Let me explain, as simply as possible, the lengthy process of making cheddar. Once the starter and rennet have been added to the milk, it coagulates and forms a junket which is cut by knives to separate it into curds and whey. These are then 'scalded' at a temperature of 104–106°F until the desired acidity level is reached. The whey is drained off and the curds cool, then are cut into large rectangular pieces ready for 'cheddaring'. This is done by hand and is incredibly hard work: the curds are stacked and re-stacked and turned to assist the draining of the whey. This continues until the whey runs clean and the level of acidity is right. Next the curds are milled, salted and finally shovelled into cloth-lined moulds, ready for pressing.

Initially pressed for 24 hours, they are then grease bandaged (wrapped in a muslin cloth dipped in lard) to help form the rind on the cheese. A rind allows a cheese to breathe as it matures, but prevents mould penetration. The cheeses are stored and turned until ready to eat; which for a mild cheese could be as little as nine months and for an extra-mature as long as 18 months. Montgomery's Cheddar is eating particularly well at the moment. Recently I tried a relatively young cheese, and it was a triumph. Creamy, tangy, it hit the teeth at first bite and then generously opened out to reveal a lingering rich flavour. Direct from the farm, you can buy a 6lb truckle at £3.60 per pound, or a large slice from a whole cheese. He is not really set up for mail order, so you may prefer to buy from Neal's Yard Dairy (see below).

Neal's Yard Dairy
6 Park Street, London, SE1 9AB
Tel: 0171 407 1800 Fax: 0171 378 0400
Contact: Caroline Howell. Last orders: 15 December. Switch, Delta, MasterCard, Visa. Delivery charge: £6 for any order.

Neal's Yard Dairy, with a shop at 17 Shorts Gardens, Covent Garden, London WC2H 9AT, is the place for enthusiasts of on-farm British cheeses from – and only from – small-scale makers for whom cheese making remains a craft. Regular customers know what a treat is in store. A visit here is like walking into a cheese heaven, with so much to choose from, sample and savour. Cheeses are in peak condition, as this is one of the very few cheese shops that is not only air-conditioned but also ripens or matures its wares in state-of the-art humidity- and temperature-controlled cellars.

'Cheese,' says owner Randolph Hodgson, 'can be variable. So we like our customers to taste and we like to tell them what we think is eating really well at that moment.' Mindful of the service offered to personal shoppers, Randolph has developed it for mail order. If you ring the dedicated line, Caroline Howell will be on hand to guide you through the range, advising what is really special and offering a bespoke service.

Of course there are classics that customers clamour for at Christmas. Whole Stiltons from Colston Bassett (see also page 122) are collected by Randolph and ripened to perfection for 12 to 18 weeks. 'I like my Stilton mellow, creamy and subtly and gently blue. These are the cheeses I select and the cheeses we sell.' With a quarter cheese, cut in the round, weighing around 4lbs and costing £21, he explains, 'buying direct from the farm may be cheaper. But we give our customers the cheeses exactly in the condition they want.' Cheddar is another favourite. Randolph's gut feeling is that Montgomery's Cheddar (see page 125) will be absolutely superb this Christmas. He has matured the huge wheels on for 24 months but will cut a piece to any size.

If you prefer a small truckle, he stocks Keen's Cheddar, also unpasteurised, but: 'the problem here is that if you age them to get any decent flavour, they're quite dry – getting on for a Parmesan. But we have plenty of old boys who adore them. They like a blast of flavour and a cheese with a good chew.' Far better, Randolph advises, to buy a 3lb truckle of Mrs Kirkham's Lancashire costing around £18, which is 'stunning'; or a 2lb-ish truckle of Appleby's Cheshire at £19.60. These he matures for a spicier flavour, 'so it goes from an innocent sharp cheese to one with more guts'.

Failing any of the above, there are creamy mould-ripened Bonchesters, rind-washed Milleens, or Gabriel, a 2-year-plus cheese that eats like a mountain Gruyère. To go with the cheese there are packets of Orkney oatcakes, floppy Staffordshire oatcakes and 8oz packs of whey butter from either Appleby's, Keen's or Duckett's, the makers of Caerphilly. Believe me, there are British specialities to satisfy even the most discerning of customers.

Ticklemore Cheese
I Ticklemore Street, Totnes, Devon, TQ9 5EJ
Tel: 01803 865926 Fax: 01803 732737
Contact: Sarie Cooper. Last orders: 1 December. No credit cards. Delivery charge: £4.50 per kilo.

Traditionalists will stick by their Stilton, but if you are after a change – albeit not a too radical one – try one of Robin Congdon's incomparable blue cheeses: Beenleigh Blue from ewes' milk, Harbourne Blue from goats' milk, or Devon Blue from Ayrshire cows' milk.

All his three cheeses are made in more or less the same way. The milk is flash-heated, started and renneted, and a mould (*Penicillium roquefortii*) is added. His is the French style of making, so Robin spikes his cheeses after a matter of days, leaves them to blue, then wraps them in foil to stop the rind. In contrast, Stilton is matured first to allow a hard crust to form, then spiked to encourage the bluing. These subtle but important differences in technique result in very differently textured cheeses. Robin's are crumbly, whereas Stilton is softer and more paste-like.

Beenleigh Blue has a crumbly, creamy texture with an immediate salty, sharp tang, and opens out to reveal a full richness with marked echoes of sheep. Devon Blue, light yellow in colour, is slightly drier with a definite crumb and the merest hint of lemon honey. The pale creamy white Harbourne has a strong sharpness that dies away quite quickly, revealing an edge of blue tempered with milky sweetness.

For a show on the table, you can buy half of any one of the above three cheeses. They weigh around 3lb and cost approximately £25.

You may prefer a special pack at £20, made up of a pound of each of the three blues plus a pound each of the hard-pressed goats' milk Ticklemore, with its creamy, mildly acid flavour and the ewes' milk Ticorino that, at first bite, is almost caramelly, then dies away with a warm fullness. Robin, it has to be said, is one of our great cheese makers.

Wild Food Tamed

31–2 Lower Horsehall Hill Cottages, Chisbury, Marlborough, Wiltshire, SN8 3HX
Tel: 01672 870639
Contact: Louisa Maskell. Last orders: 12 December. No credit cards. Delivery charge: delivery by arrangement.

Louisa Maskell lives at the edge of Savernake Forest, down at the end of a leafy track in an enchanting, idyllic cottage. A naturally inventive cook with an intuitive sense of flavour, she is also passionate about using indigenous ingredients. From spring to autumn, you may come across her loaded down with baskets filled with leaves, nuts and berries gathered from the forest.

She makes fruit cheeses in the traditional style of a thick paste. These are, by her admission, 'so good tempered that they go with everything but particularly ham or cheese'. The ingredients may vary with the seasons but always include English fruit. At this time of year she keeps in stock elderberry and apple, blackberry and apple, spiced plum, and damson with kernels. The latter is a shiny ruby-red confection, tart – Louisa by her own admission does not like sweet things – and bursting with ripe fruitiness. A 227g tub costs £2.70, and you can either arrange to pick them up in Wiltshire or Louisa can deliver them if you live in London.

Hams

Chesterton Farm Shop

Chesterton Lane, Cirencester, Gloucestershire, GL7 6JP
Tel: 01285 642160 Fax: 01285 653133
Contact: Gary Wallace. Last orders: 28 November. No credit cards. Delivery charges: next day delivery before 10 am, £20.27; before 1 pm, £13.22.

Gary Wallace of the Chesterton Farm Shop mainly sells rare-breed meat. The rare-breed animals are fed and kept 'naturally', and finished to his specifications in units dotted around the country, before being sent off for slaughter. Gary is in favour of rare-breed meat because, although its conformation is different to conventional breeds (generally it tends to be smaller) and its fat cover often heavier, there is no beating it for texture and flavour. In the case of pork, this is markedly so. The breeds

Gary deals in are Gloucester Old Spots, the traditional orchard pig, the ginger Tamworth, and the pricked-eared and particularly slow-maturing British Lop.

For the hams he has three distinctive cures, and each breed is cured in more or less the same way; but he is happy for you to specify the breed. Traditional Dry-Cure is the plainest of all the cures. The ham is massaged with salt to extract the juices, then matured for up to three weeks. Sweet Cure has the additions of brown sugar and honey for, not surprisingly, a sweeter finish; and both these hams are available either smoked over oak chips or unsmoked.

Bradenham ham is immersed in a brine flavoured with molasses, brown sugar and juniper berries for about seven days. Then it is flattened between boards to give it its longer, narrower shape, and left for three weeks before it is finally smoked. The hams have great character and good yielding texture. They are sold on the bone, with a whole ham weighing 16–20lb costing £55; or as half hams.

The Country Victualler

Winkburn Hall, Newark, Nottinghamshire, NG22 8PQ

Tel: 01636 636465 Fax: 01636 636717 email: @alderton.co.uk

Contact: Richard Craven-Smith-Milnes. Last orders: 15 December.

MasterCard, Visa, Amex, Diners. Delivery charge: for orders under £50, £10.

When it comes to ham there are two schools of thought: one is that you must buy the best quality, welfare-friendly-reared, breed-specific pig; the other is that more or less any pig will do, and it is how you cure and cook it that really matters. Richard Craven-Smith-Milnes belongs to the latter school. That is not to say that he does not choose his hams carefully, but he never specifies the breed or worries about how they are reared. 'What is important for curing is the texture of the meat.' As he admits, 'it's difficult to put into words what we it is we are looking for, and far easier to tell when it's wrong. Sometimes we get meat that's so watery, you know it won't take a cure or keep in its flavour. As for fat cover, 95 per cent of our customers don't want fat, so we go for a leaner pig. For the rest that do, we try and sort it out for them.

To cure his hams, first Richard injects them with a sugar and brine solution and then they are brined for two days. Now you may have heard dubious reports about brine-injecting to pump up the ham, but Richard assures me that he injects only to speed up the process, and anyway cooks out all the excess water. Once brined, the hams are hung for ten days to give the salts time to spread out, then they are steam-cooked for three hours, coated with their flavours and then dry roasted for four hours. It is in the dry roasting that the secret of his hams' flavour lies; many producers just flash roast so the coating adheres to the skin, 'purely for cosmetic purposes. If you dry-roast the flavour permeates right through'.

The Alderton ham is his favourite. This comes as a whole cooked ham on the bone, covered with a lush, tangy coating of marmalade. Moist, firm textured with a good bitter-sweet finish, an 11lb ham costs £66 and a 13lb ham costs £76. If the idea of carving your meat off the bone puts you off, you may prefer to try a boned Victuallers. This has a glossy honey, marmalade and Guinness finish, and costs £70 for a whole ham weighing at least 10½lb, and £36 for half a ham.

Dukeshill Ham Co Ltd
Deuxhill, Bridgnorth, Shropshire, WV16 6AF
Tel: 01746 789519 Fax: 01746 789533
Contact: George Morley. Last orders: 10 December. MasterCard, Visa.
Delivery charge: prices include p&p.

George Morley's mother was a Marsh of Marsh & Baxter, one of the great producers of York ham. So it seems only natural then when he left the family company he should start his own business specialising in what George likes to think of as 'the smoked salmon of the meat trade: York ham'.

He buys in legs of pork with a good fat cover ('for curing, it's important they're not hyper lean'), and dry cures them for three weeks in salt and saltpetre, brushing off and changing the cure three times. The hams are hung to mature for about 12 weeks until ready, and have a markedly deep, meaty resonance and a firm chew to the meat. They can be matured longer, but according to George this will affect not so much their taste as their texture, which becomes even denser, due no doubt to the moisture loss. He starts off the process with 20lb legs, but by the time they have been cured, matured, cooked (he will sell uncooked hams), skinned and trimmed, the hams weigh around 13lb. Last Christmas's price was £65, although as George says, 'with pig prices on the move I won't know exactly how much they cost until late autumn.' Traditionally, a York ham is presented at table modestly dressed with no more than breadcrumbs pressed into the outer layer of fat, so George also supplies a packet of fresh crumbs with each ham.

You may not be aware of this, but since Harris-Leeming Bar stopped curing Bradenham hams, you can no longer buy them anywhere. The Bradenham, a dark-skinned ham that is dry-cured and pickled in molasses with various spices including juniper, is one of Britain's famous traditional hams, but it is also a trade mark that Harris-Leeming Bar somehow acquired. So although the Shropshire Black ham made by George is as near to any Bradenham as you will ever get, he is not allowed to call it that. Fans of the Bradenham will recognise its pungent flavour backed up with a sweet-saltiness. Sold as a whole ham, cooked and skinned, weighing around 13lb, last year's price was £75.

The fainter-stomached may prefer the Wiltshire cure. This time George brines the hams, then hangs then for two weeks. Milder, sweeter and moist, they are very pleasant but perhaps lack the character of the dry-cured hams. Sold as whole hams, cooked in a bag with brown sugar to keep them moist and sweet, they cost £48 last year for a 13lb ham.

Incidentally, all George's ham are sold on the bone because that is how he thinks hams should be; boning them does not, in his opinion, do them any good. If pushed, however, he will bone them for you.

Emmett's Store

Peasenhall, Saxmundham, Suffolk, IP17 2HJ

Tel: 01728 660250 Fax: 01728 660404

Contact: Nigel Jerrey. Last orders: 10 December. No credit cards. Delivery charge: £8.95 per order.

Nigel Jerrey cures his Suffolk hams at the back of his general village store. As you arrive, it looks like a thousand other village shops you find in the countryside. The only hint that something special might be going on here is the royal warrant (granted by HRH the Queen Mother) hanging above the entrance. And yes, she does order her hams here.

Traditionally, a Suffolk ham is pickled in black treacle, sugar, salt and stout (Nigel uses Guinness) after it has been brined in salt, saltpetre and water. The skin turns a rich mahogany brown, and the meat is permeated with a gentle sweetness. For the best of all hams the balance must be right – neither too salty nor too sweet – and Nigel's Suffolk-cure also packs a meaty punch with a firm texture. If they sound a trifle strong, you may perhaps be tempted by his Cider-pickled ham, in which cider substitutes for the stout. The difference is remarkable, making for a lighter, gentler, fruitier ham.

New last Christmas was the Vintage Velvet, a pickle developed by Nigel in which one part of port is mixed with five parts of Guinness. I have not tried it yet, and cannot help wondering just how sweet (perhaps too much so?) the ham will taste. All Nigel's hams are smoked over oak for about five days (you can order them unsmoked), and cost £3.25 a pound. A whole ham weighs between 14 and 22lb, and a half ham between 8 and 10lb.

To cook them , Nigel recommends soaking his hams overnight in water, then sealing them in a large piece of foil with about 2 inches of water and baking them in an oven at 180C°/350F°/gas mark 4 for about 25 minutes to the pound.

Heal Farm Meats

Kings Nympton, Umberleigh, Devon, EX37 9TB

Tel: 01769 574341 Fax: 01769 572839

Contact: Anne Petch. Last orders: 9 December. Switch, Delta, MasterCard, Visa. Delivery charge: £8.50 for any order.

Anne Petch's hams are superb; some even say the best in Europe. Cured from the rare-breed pigs she rears – Gloucester Old Spot, Middle White, russet-red Tamworth, Berkshire, Large Black, Saddleback with their distinctive stripe, and British Lop – they have a deep succulence, a bracing meatiness and a firm texture. Whether there is any difference of flavour between the breeds, Anne is none too sure. 'All our pigs get fed the same feed and drink the same water, so the flavour is more or less the same. Where there are differences, they tend to be in the conformation. A Middle White makes little round chubby hams, whereas a Tamworth's ham is far more streamlined and elongated, with a fine texture.'

One advantage of rare-breed ham, or disadvantage depending on how you view the matter, is its fat. Some breeds put on more than others but, as most of us know, for the meat to have true flavour and moistness you need fat both as an outer layer and as marbling through the actual muscle. 'In fact,' says Anne, 'their fat cover is on average only about half an inch at the thickest point, tapering to nothing. But as I offer a bespoke butchery service, my customers can specify exactly how they like their hams trimmed, and which breed of pig.'

Her hams are brine-cured in salt, saltpetre and water ('because the flavour of the meat is so outstanding that this is the best way to bring it out') for seven to fourteen days depending on their size, and then hung for three to four weeks while the process carries on. A whole ham weighs 3.5–4.5kg, halves 1.5–3.0kg, and you can order them smoked for around 60 hours over oak, or unsmoked, raw, or either plainly or cider cooked with spices and brown sugar, then skinned and coated in toasted wholemeal breadcrumbs. Sold on the bone, prices range from £10.83 per kilo for a raw unsmoked ham, to £13.92 per kilo for a smoked cider-cooked ham.

Mooreland Foods

Vost Farm, Morley Green, Wilmslow, Cheshire, SK9 5NU

Tel: 01625 548499 Fax: 01625 548606

Contact: John Ward. Last orders: 10 December. Switch, Delta, MasterCard, Visa, Amex, Diners. Delivery charge: £6.50 for overnight carriage; minimum order £25.

Mooreland Foods – curers and smokers of fine foods – is a proper family business. It was John Ward's grandfather who started it, and now it is in the safe hands of John and his son Darren. Recently they moved to new premises, with a shop and café out front and state-of-the-art processing rooms and three 18-foot high, 7-foot deep smokeholes behind that look as if they have been in use since grandfather's day. 'They're built to his design. And before you can start using them, you have to fire them off. It took us weeks. It's like seasoning a wok: unless it's properly done the food won't cook properly. In a unseasoned chimney, it doesn't get a true smoked flavour and comes out all wishy-washy.'

John describes Cheshire as 'one big pig area'. 'But the hardest job is selecting the right animal. For bacon and ham we need a bit of cover – fat – and we end up rejecting so much. Most pork is either too lean or too watery or both. We find the right size with the right fatness comes from Large White Landrace cross.' When they can get them, the Wards also buy rare-breed pigs such as Tamworths, Berkshire and Gloucester Old Spot. 'We do charge a little more for their products and the meat can contain more fat – we say good cover – but you will find the flavour to be excellent and superior to other breeds.'

Whatever the breed, the pork is processed in the same way. Slaughtered off-site, it comes to the unit for butchering. Then the meat is dry-cured in a mixture of salt, sugar and saltpetre. 'Just rubbed in the good old fashioned way and left to stand. Once cured and hung to dry, there is a weight loss of around 20 per cent of the original weight.' Most commercial or large-scale curers inject their meat with a brine solution of up to 20 per cent of its original weight, pumping it up with polyphosphates and goodness knows what else. Darren even told me of a manufacturer using potato starch. This solution is absorbed by the meat, although curiously enough, legally they only have to declare 10 per cent added water. 'Of course it makes it very difficult to compete on price. They only have to declare 10 per cent; but if you think about it we are actually 40 per cent down. But then our bacon won't weep, splutter and shrink in the pan.'

The hams are impressive. York ham is elongated and sleek and butchered in a traditional long cut to take in the oyster. Dry-cured for about five weeks, it is matured for three months and then either sold raw or slowly steamed, lightly roasted and sent off with a packet of breadcrumbs for pressing into the trimmed layer of outer fat. A whole cooked ham usually weighs around 15lb, and costs £58.

New this year is the Cavendish that the Wards have developed in conjunction with Sandy Boyd of Chatsworth Farm Shop (see page 135). The same long cut as for the York is dry cured for four weeks, soaked in what sounds like a heady mixture of molasses, cracked coriander, juniper berries and black peppercorns, then matured for three months. The Wards like to think of the Cavendish as being a close relation of the now-defunct Bradenham (it is no longer being made commercially) , but as I have not tried it I cannot comment. If it is as good as their other hams, however, it will be superb.

Finally their Mooreland ham deserves a mention; it is different from all the others as it is eaten in its raw state. Dry-cured for 6 to 8 weeks, soaked in honey, molasses and a few spices for about a month, then matured for almost a year, its secret lies in the maturation where 'temperature and humidity are all important'. Subtle and sweet, with what I can only describe as a meaty clean taste, it has a chewy texture with a good length of flavour and is sold in 8oz and 4oz sliced packs costing £5.50 and £3.75 respectively.

Rannoch Smokery
Kinloch Rannoch, Pitlochry, Tayside, PH16 5QD
Tel: 01882 632344 Fax: 01882 632441
Contact: Leo Barclay. Last orders: 12 December. MasterCard, Visa. Delivery charge: £1.60 per 250g; overnight delivery on request.

For a punchy flavour of game, you should try the succulent venison ham from Rannoch Smokery. Using haunch from wild red deer, it is cured in salt, sugar and saltpetre brine, and hot-smoked to cook it through over oak chips cut from whisky barrels. A whole boned ham weighs around 3kg and costs £19.20 per kilo, but they will cut it to any weight you require. If you prefer it ready-sliced they also sell it in 100g and 250g packs costing £3.30 and £8.00 respectively.

Richard Woodall
Lane End, Waberthwaite, Nr Millom, Cumbria, LA19 5YJ
Tel: 01229 717237 Fax: 01229 717007
Contact: Richard Woodall. Last orders: 5 December. MasterCard, Visa. Delivery charge: 5kg or less, £4.70; over 5kg, £6.

A seventh-generation Woodall, Richard (Bar) to his friends, his wife June and nephew Colin run the bacon, sausage and ham business from a village shop that doubles as a sub-post office.

Made with a great sense of tradition, their products are without doubt among the best in the country. Most of the meat comes from the pig farm run by Bar's brother. Since 1976 it has been a closed herd (meaning that they do not buy in stock and only breed from within the herd) of Landrace and Large White pigs. Reared on a semi-intensive system, they are fed an antibiotic-free diet of cereal and vegetable proteins. 'Control of the raw material is essential. We aim for a consistency of size, and obviously it gives us the great advantage of being able to process when the meat is really fresh.'

Their range may be limited but it is outstanding. Curing is done in the old-fashioned way with a dry salt-cure. Once, before brining (Wiltshire-cure) was introduced, this was how all pork was cured for bacon and ham. Basically the meat is rubbed all over with a mixture of salt and saltpetre and left for several days (14 in Bar's case). It works on the principle that as liquid comes out of the meat it dissolves the salt, which in turn is absorbed by the meat, causing more of its water to flow out. This is a slow and expensive process, and when done properly it cannot be hurried. The meat is then washed and hung by Bar to mature for as long as deemed necessary.

Bar's Cumberland ham, cured for a month, washed and dried, and matured for three months, has a full-bodied meaty character. Its texture, similar to a York ham, is resilient, with plenty of bite. These he will supply more or less how you want them: whole or half hams, bone-in or boned, smoked or unsmoked, raw or cooked, skinned and dressed with brown sugar and cloves. A straightforward whole bone-in ham weighs around 15lb and costs £3.15 a pound. His pricing then becomes rather complicated, adding an extra 41p per pound for smoking (over oak for two days) or £1.02 for cooking (boiled in a bag to keep them moist), I think I will leave you to work it out. Incidentally, if all you want is a tiny ham joint – no more than a couple of pounds, but enough to give a feel of festivity to the sideboard – Bar will supply those too.

Cumbria air-dried ham is a relatively recent invention. Here the ham is dry-cured for a month in salt, saltpetre, herbs and a few spices (Bar has always been reticent about the exact ingredients), then air-dried (matured) for 12 months, for a punchy but succulent meat. Cumbria Mature Royal is pickled in beer, treacle, sugar vinegar and salt for a month, lightly smoked, then matured for 12 months. Both are sold thinly sliced and eaten like Parma ham, that is to say in their raw state. They come either as whole hams (tricky to slice thinly enough, unless you have a machine), or in 4 and 8oz ready-sliced packs.

Other meats and pies

Chatsworth Farm Shop

Stud Farm, Pilsley, Bakewell, Derbyshire, DE45 1UF

Tel: 01246 583392 Fax: 01246 583464

Contact: Sandy Boyd. Last orders: 14 December. Switch, Visa, Amex. Delivery charge: £9.50 for all next-day fresh delivieries.

Chatsworth Farm Shop, winner of this year's Best Specialist Shop in the Good Food Awards, has a well-deserved reputation for excellence. Run by Sandy Boyd, it sells only British produce chosen with quality in mind and sourced from the farm, either Chatsworth itself or tenant or local farms, or from the smaller food producers scattered around the country.

Attached to the enticing shop is the kitchen. Under the supervision of chef André, who used to cook at the House, it produces a tempting array of own products that includes jams, cakes, puddings (see also page 72) and a range of cold cutting-pies. Best-seller is the very handsome game pie. It comes with the warning 'this is a natural country pie and may contain shot'. And, as if to prove just how 'natural and country' it is, they are also unwilling to specify exactly with which game and in what quantities it is made. Usually you will find venison, pheasant, wild duck and rabbit and plenty of it. A whole pie weighs about 1.8kg and costs £18.

Derbyshire Pork, a variation on the conventional pork pie in that it contains walnuts, sultanas and apple for a sweeter, fruitier taste, costs £12 for a 1.8kg pie. Duck with apricot also has that satisfying balance of savoury with sweet. And finally, new this year (and so new I have not even tasted it) is rabbit with gin. To ensure the pies arrive in perfect condition, they are made with butter shortcrust rather than a hot-water crust pastry, and vacuum-packed. And, as Sandy advises, make sure you open the pies a good hour before serving, to allow the pastry to crispen up.

Also prepared in the kitchens, and a really good standby, is the potted beef. Made in the 'proper' way by pounding the beef with butter and spices, this is a perennial favourite. A 454g tub costs £2.20.

The Old Smokehouse and Truffles

Brougham Hall, Brougham, Penrith, Cumbria, CA10 2DE

Tel: 01768 867772 Fax: 01768 867772

Contact: Rona Newsom. Last orders: 5 December. No credit cards. Delivery charge: prices include p&p.

Rona Newsom's smokehouse is rather romantically set in the courtyard of Brougham Hall, an old castle that was converted in the 19th century. Using a modern Afos kiln, she smokes a whole range of products such as chicken, game and fish, and her style is a light cure and a mild smoke that ensures that the intrinsic flavour of the ingredient shines through.

If you are looking for something a little different for the sideboard over the holidays, you should try the smoked Herdwick Lamb. Herdwick is the local breed of lamb (see Agnus Quality Meats, page 48), and for smoking Rona uses a boned and rolled shoulder. First she brines it for about three days in salt, sugar, pickling spices and garlic, then she rubs it all over with a fiery oil mixed with pepper, paprika and cayenne, adding sprigs of fresh rosemary. This is then cold-smoked for about five hours, and then hot-smoked to cook it through 'until it is done'. Streaked through with a clear tasting fat, the round slices of meat are slightly pink, tender and juicy with the marked sweetness of lamb punched with rosemary, but with only the barest hint of smoke. Sold in whole pieces weighing around 1kg, it costs £23 including a jar of locally made Cumberland sauce to serve with it.

Equally inventive, if not quite as unusual, is the cold smoked beef. Using topside butchered like a fillet and trimmed of all fat, Rona cures this for three to five days, this time in a brine flavoured with juniper and bay leaf. Then it is rubbed in a spiced oil, hung to dry for about 12 hours and finally cold-smoked for no more than five hours, as 'it is important not to over-smoke it'. Rona prefers to sell this in whole pieces weighing about 1kg at £23.50. This means you can slice it as thinly as you wish. The easiest way to achieve wafer-thin slices is, apparently, to put the piece in the freezer for about half an hour before you cut it.

Ye Olde Pork Pie Shoppe

10 Nottingham Street, Melton Mowbray, Leicestershire, LE13 1NW

Tel: 01664 62341 Fax: 01664 62341

Contact: Stephen Hallam. Last orders: 22 December. No credit cards. Personal shoppers only; list of stockists available on request.

I once had a boyfriend with the most peculiar appetite: Christmas breakfast had to be Melton Mowbray pork pie washed down with buck's fizz. I can see this is a highly individualistic preference, although in its favour it does set you up if there is a long wait ahead for the main meal. Most people, though, order their pies for Boxing Day.

Proper Melton Mowbray pork pies are made with a boiled paste of flour, lard, salt and water that is hand raised around a dolly (cylindrical wooden block) from start to finish. At Ye Olde Pork Pie Shoppe, they do now use machinery, but Stephen Hallam assured me that all the pies are finished by hand. They also have a particularly distinctive shape. Unlike other pork pies with their straight-up-and-down sides and neatly tucked top, a Melton Mowbray top has wavy edges and bows and bulges like a pot belly. This is because it is hand crimped, baked without a hoop or tin, and therefore completely self supporting. Appearance is important: 'Not only must it look right so you know it's authentic, but it also affects the way the filling cooks. We aim for a pie that is not just a rich pastry holding up a meat filling or a meaty filling enclosed in pastry, but a perfect marriage of the two.'

The ingredients for the filling are also of prime importance. When pies were first baked in Melton Mowbray, they probably used meat from the Tamworth pig, the local breed fattened on whey, a by-product from Stilton, the local cheese. Now Stephen uses good quality lean pork. It is hand chopped for a good texture, and unlike most other pork pies it is always used fresh rather than cured. This means that when you cut it open the filling may look dull and grey rather than the vibrant pink of cured meat. But try it. The flavour is fuller and it packs a peppery punch which Stephen assures me is the tradition. The pies are made up with equal weights of meat and pastry. Once cooked, each pie is pricked and hand filled with a proper own-made stock made from split pigs' trotters which, once cooled, turns to succulent jelly. Pies of 1lb and 2lb are baked freshly every day, and cost £2.59 and £5.18 respectively.

Old-Fashioned Spiced Beef

Serves 6–8

Spiced beef is traditional to the days after Christmas. This simple but subtle recipe can be prepared using salt meat, which is available from good butchers who keep 'a brine on the go'.

1.25–1.75kg (3–4lb) joint of boned salt silverside or brisket
15ml (1 tbsp) whole allspice
15ml (1 tbsp) juniper berries
10ml (1 dsp) cloves
15ml (1 tbsp) black peppercorns
75g (3oz) soft dark brown muscovado sugar

Soak the beef in cold water for 2 to 4 hours, changing the water once or twice. Put the whole allspice, juniper berries, cloves and black peppercorns into a grinder or pestle and mortar, and grind until fine. Then mix in a bowl with the brown sugar. Press this mixture all over the joint, into any cracks of the meat and make one or two incisions in the meat to get the mixture right to the centre.

Wrap the joint very thoroughly in two layers of foil, to catch the juices that are released as it cooks. Place the wrapped joint in a large ovenproof dish with a tight-fitting lid, or in a roasting tray with more foil on top. If possible leave it at room temperature overnight.

Preheat the oven to 140°C/275°F/gas mark 1. Roast the joint in the centre of the oven for 3½–5 hours, allowing about 70 minutes per 500g (1lb) until cooked through. After 3½ hours the meat will be pink, but you can cook it longer if you prefer more well-done meat. Remove from the oven and open the foil slightly to let the juice pour away, then wrap the foil round the joint again. Leave the joint in a cool place with a board and one or two heavy books or weights on top of it until the next day. To serve, carve into as thin slices as possible.

From *Sainsbury's Christmas Book* by Josceline Dimbleby
(J Sainsbury)

Pickles and chutneys

The Bay Tree Food Company

Lower Westcombe Farm, Evercreech, Shepton Mallet, Somerset, BA4 6ER
Tel: 01749 831300 Fax: 01749 831233 email: thebaytree@dial.pipex.com
Contact: Lucie Green. Last orders: 7 December. Switch, Delta, MasterCard, Visa. Delivery charge: p&p extra.

The Bay Tree Food Company produces imaginative and finely judged chutneys, relishes, pickles and preserved fruits. Everything is made in small batches, to preserve texture and flavour and to ensure an even cooking. Sometimes, when deemed necessary, pickles are aged to allow the flavours to meld and mellow out.

From the range of chutneys and pickles is a fruity redcurrant and pear chutney costing £2.95 for a 310g jar. With a good texture (you get both the skins and pips of the redcurrants), it is quite sharp to act as a good foil to a rich cold meat. Cucumber relish is charming, made with fresh cucumbers left to salt in bowls, then mixed in a marinade of distilled malt vinegar, sugar, pickling spice and cinnamon. It has a crisp texture and a fresh sweet-sour flavour, and costs £4.50 for a 220g kilner jar; or you can buy a plastic refill sleeve at £3.45 for 300g to decant it into a jar of your own.

Boxing Day (apricot and coriander) or Festive Day (onions, prunes and raisins) chutneys may need no introduction, but what is new and innovative is the Bay Tree Food Company's range of preserved fruit. There are spiced oranges that come wafer-thin in a thick sweet-sour syrup sharpened with white wine vinegar and spiced with chilli and mixed spices; or either whole or sliced, softly-textured preserved lemons with a resoundingly salty bite, and a cunning mixture of sweet and sharp. Serve all these with cold meats and poultry, or, in the case of marinated figs (made with dried baby figs soaked in white wine, rum, sugar, mixed spice, cinnamon, vanilla and lemon), with ice cream or yoghurt. Prices start at £5.50 for a 380g kilner jar.

Iranian Pickled Shallots

Lindsey Bareham swears by her recipe for pickled shallots, taken from her book *Onions Without Tears* (Penguin). Every year, she makes a jar a couple of weeks before Christmas, and serves them on the days after to go with cold cuts. Fills a 900g (2lb) jar.

450g (1lb) Thai shallots or small shallots, peeled and broken into their natural halves
15 garlic cloves

4 sprigs fresh mint
570ml (1pt) white wine or cider vinegar
18ml (3½ tsp) salt

Cut a deep cross into each shallot or shallot section, so that it is almost quartered but stays attached at the bottom. Fill a hot, sterilised wide-mouth jar with the shallots, stacking them on top of each other. Place the garlic and mint in the bowl of a blender or food processor. Start the motor and add the vinegar little by little with the salt, and mix thoroughly. Pour the spiced vinegar into a saucepan, bring to the boil, then pour over the onions. Allow to cool, seal and keep for two weeks before using.

Wendy Brandon
Felin Wen, Boncath, Pembrokeshire, SA37 OJR
Tel: 01239 841568 Fax: 01239 841746
Contact: Wendy Brandon. Last orders: 15 December. MasterCard, Visa.
Delivery charge: £5.75 for any size of order.

Wendy Brandon's preserves and chutneys veer towards the unusual. Inventive in the combinations of ingredients and the judicious use of spices, they make a welcome addition to any ham, cold cut or pie on the Christmas sideboard. Her Green Bean chutney, made with sliced, carefully spiced green beans lightly thickened with cornflour, has a crisp texture and a gentle sweetness. Pickled Dried Fruit is a cunning combination of baby dried figs soaked in one of Wendy's red-currant fruit vinegars, spiced with cinnamon.

As for her mustards, sold in 225g jars and costing £2.80, these too are highly individual. Honey Mustard, hot, sweet and smooth, is made with mustard flour sweetened with honey and flavoured with a mixture of spices. Fruit mustards, which she claims as her own invention, are best described as half-way between a mustard and a chutney. They come in a choice of various fruits including lemon, orange, blueberry, blackberry, blackcurrant and red currant. Here the whole fruit is lightly boiled, then mixed with either whole grain mustard or mustard flour, depending on the texture of the fruit. 'If the fruit has seeds, then I use a mustard flour, otherwise I use mustard seed to introduce a texture.' Well fruited, they also have the gentle kick of a well-rounded mustard.

Mrs Huddleston's Luxury Home-made Provisions

13 The Green, Mentmore, Buckinghamshire, LU7 0QF

Tel: 01296 661423 Fax: 01296 661423

email: 310072.3646@compuserve.com

Contact: Christine Huddleston. Last orders: 4 December. No credit cards.

Delivery charge: £3.50 minimum charge.

Christine Huddleston has been making preserves in a small commercial way for about a year. She describes her products as 'for a grown-up taste, neither too sweet nor too dull'. Still experimenting, she is building up her repertoire. 'Some things I repeat with exactitude, others I may play around with.'

Everything is made in small batches in the 'old fashioned' way, using good quality ingredients. Worth remembering to go with a ham or Stilton is the Christmas chutney. Reasonably firm, it is a spiced mixture of various dried fruits, including figs, apricots, and prunes 'to give it depth and colour', and sharpened with cider vinegar. Then there are the different jellies. These vary, but the ginger wine struck me as a thoroughly good idea. Nearly all the jars cost around £2.50 and weigh 8oz.

Christmas Club Sandwich

Serves 2

A club sandwich is the ideal way to use up any leftovers. It is best made with interesting bread: sourdough, wholewheat or a good baguette.

4 slices of thick-cut bacon
2 egg yolks
30ml (2 tbsp) lemon juice
150ml (¼pt) olive oil
150ml (¼pt) sunflower oil
45g (1½oz) Stilton or other blue cheese
2 medium tomatoes
5ml (1 tsp) balsamic vinegar
½ avocado pear
small bunch of flat-leaf parsley
6 slices of good bread (see above)
4 slices of cooked turkey
salt and freshly ground black pepper

Grill the bacon until crisp. Meanwhile make the mayonnaise in a food processor by whizzing the egg yolks with 15ml (1 tbsp) of lemon juice. Mix the oils together and then, with the machine still running, trickle them in and process until thick and creamy. Add the Stilton and a teaspoon of lemon juice, and whizz again until the cheese is well mixed in. Adjust the seasoning.

Slice the tomatoes and sprinkle with vinegar. Peel and slice the avocado and sprinkle with lemon juice. Chop the parsley. Cut each bacon rasher in half.

Spread two slices of bread on one side with mayonnaise and scatter over a little parsley. Put the bacon and avocado on top. Scatter over more parsley, and season to taste. Spread two more slices of bread on both sides with the mayonnaise and lay these on top.

Arrange half of the tomato slices on the bread. Top with turkey, then add the remaining tomato and season. Finally, spread the remaining two slices of bread on one side with the mayonnaise and lay them, spread side down, on top. Secure each sandwich with an orange stick, and serve.

From *Fast Food for Friends* by Lewis Esson with Henrietta Green and Marie-Pierre Moine (Conran Octopus)

Party Food

The Country Victualler

Winkburn Hall, Newark, Nottinghamshire, NG22 8PQ

Tel: 01636 636465 Fax: 01636 636717 email: @alderton.co.uk

Contact: Richard Craven-Smith-Milnes. Last orders: 15 December.

MasterCard, Visa, Amex, Diners. Delivery charge: for orders under £50, £10.

Although Richard Craven-Smith-Milnes refers to his gutsy wild boar with juniper berries as a pâté *en croute*, I prefer to think of it as a good old fashioned cutting pie. Made with equal quantities of coarsely minced wild boar and pork flavoured with juniper berries, the meat is wrapped in a hand-raised hot-water crust and then baked in the oven. As soon as it is cooked, the pastry is pierced and ham stock is poured in to moisten the filling; as it cools it turns to jelly. A whole pie weighs 6lb, costs £36, and will yield 15 generous slices, but you can also buy halves at £18.95.

Crosse Farm Bakery

Unit 4, Cranmere Road, Exeter Road Industrial Estate, Okehampton, Devon, EX20 1QA

Tel: 01837 55457 Fax: 01837 53874

Contact: Harriet Helliwell. Last orders: 15 December. Switch, MasterCard, Visa. Delivery charge: £8 p&p for bread.

Harriet Helliwell is a firm believer that to make good cakes, pastries, puddings and breads, you need good ingredients. 'I place a lot of emphasis on the quality of my raw ingredients; if you don't, it just doesn't work.'

Her focaccia is markedly good. Made with lashings of olive oil, it is one of the best I have ever tried. Possibly an Italian might disagree, dismissing it as too thick or too bread-like, but I could not stop tearing away at it. Harriet first makes a slack dough that she leaves to rise twice, so the texture of the bread opens up to absorb the copious quantities of olive oil while baking. She flavours it with pumpkin and sunflower seeds, sun-dried tomatoes, fresh rosemary and black olives, garlic, sea salt or a mixture of any of the above. And as soon as it comes out of the oven, even more olive oil is poured over it.

She does produce it in a small (400g) size, but for mail order she only sells the 800g weight in boxes of eight – which should comfortably see you through the holidays. When I first tried it, Harriet made it in huge flat 2ft rounds. Since then, due to some vagary or other of the Weights and Measures Inspectorate, it has to be made by weight. Sadly, the new size of loaf looks just like any other chubby loaf; so when ordering, I would try and prevail on her to flatten them. Actually they are better that way: crisper and looking more like what you would expect of a focaccia.

A large loaf feeds around ten people, so is a great addition to a party's hot or cold table. It is best eaten within two days of delivery, but can be frozen for up to three months. To reheat from frozen; simply wrap it in foil and place in a pre-heated oven, 160°C/330°F/gas mark

5, for about 15 minutes. Then remove the foil and drizzle with yet more olive oil.

Joel Brioche

Unit 7, 81 Southern Row, London, W10 5AL

Tel: 0181 964 0240 Fax: 0181 964 0240

Contact: Joel Edmond. Last orders: 20 December. No credit cards. No delivery charge inside London.

Joel Edmond of the eponymous Joel Brioche is a chef cum party organiser. He will organise as much or as little as you want, or just supply food. To take the weight off your shoulders, he will deliver anywhere in London (arrangements can be made for further afield, but he warns, 'it will cost') a box of ready-made canapés. A selection of 100 made up from his list of forty or so ideas starts at £75, and might include vegetable bruschetta, filo cups filled with crab or Parmesan bread with mushrooms, but obviously you can discuss the choice.

Either for a drinks or a tea party, you may well be tempted by his brioche surprise. This takes the form of a huge brioche about 12 inches across and 11 inches high, that has been hollowed out and filled with little sandwiches made from brioche bread, with the lid arranged back on top. He has about eight flavours – cream cheese and chive, spicy tapenade, sun-dried tomato mousse – and suggests that you vary the flavours with the layers. On the other hand, you may prefer all smoked salmon or all smoked meats. And if you want to go totally over the top, he will even make lobster sandwiches, 'but at silly prices'. Prices vary according to the fillings, but a basic brioche surprise costs £75; and as that contains around 220 little sandwiches, it will feed quite a few people. Joel likes at least 72 hours' warning, and rumour has it that, unlike most caterers, he will be working between Christmas and New Year. But if I were you I would not leave it that late to order.

Konditor & Cook

22 Cornwall Road, London, SE1 8TW

Tel: 0171 261 0456 Fax: 0171 261 9021

Contact: Gerhard Jenne. Last orders: 12 December. Switch, MasterCard, Visa. Delivery charge: p&p extra.

Little savoury biscuits always go down a treat at a drinks party. And Gerhard Jenne bakes several on a daily basis. My favourites are the round mini-parmesan biscuits with a remarkable cheese resonance. Made with butter, flour, parmesan and salt, they are two-bite size with a texture that I can best describe at half-crisp, half-crumbly. If you prefer them with 'a bit of heat', try the square-shaped smoked chilli versions, which are lightly flecked with chilli. Both cost around £1.95 for a 100g packet that yields about 15 biscuits.

The Emmental cheese shortbread is lighter in texture, larger in shape but (almost) equally more-ish. These are rolled in various seeds such as poppy or caraway, for an effective crunchy finish.

Quick Canapés

Believe it or not, canapés can be quick to make if you work on the principle of a factory assembly line. First get your bases organised and spread them out on a work surface, then make the toppings. Finally put the two together by spooning the topping carefully on to the bases and pressing it down gently. And as you are working in miniature, make sure you use a teaspoon.

Bases

Most canapés need a base of some sort. For these purposes I divide them into two categories – fresh or baked.

Fresh bases can be peeled cucumber slices cut to about 1–1.25cm (½in) thick with a little of the seed hollowed out for the topping, or celery sticks filled down the centre. Also easy and quick to use as little cups are the leaves broken off a head of chicory, radicchio, Little Gem, iceberg or cos lettuce.

For baked bases, buy mini-oatcakes, pastry cups or shells, mini vol-au-vents or baby scones cut in half. A bought focaccio can be cut into small squares or any shape you fancy; baguettes or ciabatta can be cut into small slices, then lightly brushed with olive oil and baked in the oven. Alternatively you can make your own bread discs. Use ready-sliced, thinly cut bread – white or brown – and cut out little circles with a 2.5cm/1in pastry cutter. With a pastry brush, paint them all over with olive oil and bake them off in a medium oven (190°C/375°F/gas mark 5) for 10 to 15 minutes until they have crisped up and turned golden brown. They can be stored for a few days in an airtight tin.

Toppings: enough for 24 canapés

Stilton and Bacon

Mash 55g (2oz) of Stilton with a fork and stir in about 15ml (1 tbsp) of single cream. Grill 2 or 3 rashers of streaky bacon until crisp, then chop into small pieces. Spoon the cheese mixture onto a base and sprinkle the bacon on top.

Scrambled Eggs with Smoked Salmon and Dill

Make scrambled eggs with two eggs and 15g (½oz) butter. Just as the eggs are setting, remove from the heat and stir in

15ml (1 tbsp) single cream. Spoon the eggs on to a base of your choice. Cut 30g (1oz) smoked salmon into tiny strips and lay on top of the eggs. Decorate with a sprig of dill.

Ricotta and Pesto
Take 85g (3oz) ricotta cheese and mash it with 30ml (2 tbsp) of bought pesto, a touch of salt and freshly ground black pepper. Spoon on to a base of your choice, and decorate with torn basil leaves.

From *Fast Food for Friends* by Lewis Esson with Henrietta Green and Marie-Pierre Moine (Conran Octopus)

Macsween of Edinburgh
Dryden Road, Bilston Glen, Loanhead, Edinburgh, EH20 9LZ
Tel: 0131 440 2555 Fax: 0131 440 2674
Contact: Jo Macsween. Last orders: 22 December. Switch, Delta, MasterCard, Visa. Delivery charge: minimum order 1½lb, £2.55 p&p.

'More and more people are eating haggis on Hogmanay. It's easy to cook and lines your stomach before getting drunk,' says Jo Macsween with disarming honesty. With a mild meatiness and a rich nuttiness, Macsween's is moist, crumbly and spoonable. Apparently if you can slice a hot haggis, there is something very wrong with its texture.

Haggis, as you may already know, comes from sheep's pluck: the lung, heart and liver. Macsween use only a small proportion of liver, 'so it's not too livery.' The pluck is cooked and minced, and mixed with beef fat (body back fat) which is infinitely preferable to the more normal suet, because 'it doesn't cook out and keeps the meat moist and gives a much cleaner taste'. Next comes oatmeal from the Borders in two grists (cuts) – pinhead and medium – dried onions and seasoning of salt, black and white pepper, nutmeg, mace and coriander; and finally a little of the gravy from the boiling meat.

Everything is mixed together, and put into a hopper with the 'bung' (the bovine equivalent of an appendix) fixed around the nozzle. Using only natural casings, for haggis between 1lb and 5lb they use bungs, and for the sizes upwards to 18lb they use the stomach to make the traditional kidney-shaped haggis known as the Chieftain or Ceremonial. Prices range from £2.20 for a 1½lb haggis (the smallest sent by mail order) to £17.60 for an 8lb. Macsween will also supply frozen packs of neeps and tatties. Also known as clapshot, this is traditionally served with haggis along with a 'wee dram', and is mashed potato and what the Scots call turnips but southerners know as swedes.

Rather tantalising are the cocktail haggis. These come in packs of 25, and Jo lyrically describes them as 'like a string of fat pearls'. They need only the gentle treatment of steaming for a few minutes to warn them through, and cost £2.50 for the pack. Jo suggests slicing and serving them as canapés with rowanberry jelly on mini oatcakes.

Maison Blanc

37 St John's Wood High Street, London, NW8 7NJ

Tel: 0171 586 1982 Fax: 0171 586 1087

Contact: Mandy Kenyon and Cecile Sezrier. Last orders: 22 December. Switch, Delta,MasterCard, Visa, Diners. Personal shoppers only.

On Twelfth Night in France, most households serve a *galette de roi*. Based on a centuries-old French recipe, it is a round puff-pastry tart with an almond filling. While it is buttery and relatively interesting to eat, eating it is not its real point. Tucked in the filling is a *feve* (literally a bean but nowadays more often a charm). Whoever finds the *feve* in their slice gets to be king or queen for the night, wear the paper crown that is given away with the cake, and appoint a consort with whom they can generally misbehave. And as Twelfth Night signifies the end of the holidays (you must remember to take down your decorations on that day) it is the last chance for mild celebrations before work starts in earnest.

Maison Blanc, with a new shop just opened in St John's Wood High Street, London, and other branches dotted around London (in Notting Hill Gate, Chelsea, Hampstead and Richmond), and around the south (in Oxford, Cobham, Guildford and Chichester), sells a fine version with a tiny hand-painted porcelain charm. A four- to six-portion tart costs £8.50 and eight to ten portions, £13.50. Apart from Christmas Day, Boxing Day and New Year's Day, they will remain open during the holidays so you can leave it until quite late to order.

Their *pain surprise*, however, must be ordered 14 days in advance. These are hollowed-out breads shaped in such extraordinary, over-the-top shapes as *panier* (basket), *marmite* (stew-pot), lobster and crab, and for children, elephant, cow and cat. Filled with small sandwiches of just about any filling you may care to dream up, and decorated with lettuce leaves, they contain 40 or 90 sandwiches (depending on the shape you go for) and cost between £24.50 and £46.50. And should you be tempted by just the shaped bread, you can buy them empty for a mere £12.

Mooreland Foods

Vost Farm, Morley Green, Wilmslow, Cheshire, SK9 5NU

Tel: 01625 548499 Fax: 01625 548606

Contact: John Ward. Last orders: 10 December. Switch, Delta, MasterCard, Visa, Amex, Diners. Delivery charge: £6.50 for overnight carriage, minimum order £25.

All too often smoked nuts can be a bad idea. The nuts are dried-out, overpoweringly smoky and 'claw' at the back of your throat. Not so in the case of Mooreland Foods' nuts. These are gloriously rich and juicy, enhanced by the lightest touch of woodiness. You could pick at them all night.

Using best grade almonds and cashews, they are cold smoked in specially designed trays over hickory wood chippings imported from the USA. Then they are roasted (hot smoked) to give them a nutty intensity. This process takes around three hours, but as Darren tells me: 'It's difficult to tell exactly when the almonds are ready, so I constantly have to bite on them to check whether they're toasted right through. Some hardship!' As a finish the nuts are tossed in vegetable oil and salt while still warm. A 1kg bag costs £13.95, and provided you store them in an airtight container, the nuts will keep for at least a couple of months.

Mrs Elizabeth King

Hardigate Road, Cropwell Butler, Nottinghamshire, NG12 3AG

Tel: 0115 9332252 Fax: 0115 9332252

Contact: Ian Hartland. Last orders: 19 December. Delta, MasterCard, Visa.

Delivery charge: £10.99 per order.

Mrs Elizabeth King's pork pies are just what is needed to keep in the freezer as a stand-by for a party. They are delivered frozen, so you bake them off as and when needed and they will keep frozen for up to six months. The thinking behind this is to ensure maximum freshness when you want to eat them. And it works.

Each pie comes complete with baking instructions and a little sack of jelly, and I dutifully followed the instructions. First you thaw it out, then bake it for an hour (depending on size) at 200C°/400F°/gas mark 6, leave it to cool for 30 minutes, heat the jelly and pour it into the centre. You must be careful at this point: if you pour it in too enthusiastically it bubbles over, something not mentioned in the instructions. Then you have to sit back and wait for the pie to cool and, more importantly, the jelly to set. If, like me, you are too greedy to wait long enough, beware; when I cut the pie open, the jelly flooded out.

Nonetheless, the pie was very satisfactory. The hot-water pastry made with flour, water, lard and salt was crisp and clean; the pork filling, made with chopped pork shoulder, was perhaps a little solid as if it had been a trifle over-processed; but the flavour was unquestionably meaty and peppery – exactly what you would hope for from a good pork pie. With a generous balance of meat to pastry, a Banquet size weighs 5lb, yields around 30 slices and costs £13; the Party pie weighs 3lb, yields 24 slices and costs £8; and there are also 1½lb, 1lb and individual-portion pies.

R & J Lodge

4 Greens End Road, Meltham, Huddersfield, Yorkshire, HD7 3NW

Tel: 01484 850571 Fax: 01484 850571

email: www.gbdirect.co.uk/food/r&jlodge

Contact: Raymond Lodge. Last orders: 22 December. No credit cards.

Delivery charge: £6.76 for up to 5kg.

I defy any food lover to spend time in Yorkshire and leave without trying at least one meat pie, assuming of course they are not vegetarian. The better general – or specifically pork – butchers still make their own, but Raymond Lodge, a one-time butcher, now makes nothing but hand-raised pies. Although he does make pies in various sizes to sell in the shop, Raymond will only mail order a 3lb pie, which he reckons 'will cut up nicely into 20 slices', or a four-selection pack of 12oz pies.

He starts by making a hot water crust. Lard is 'melted not too hot, because it would make the pastry too hard'. He mixes it with flour and leaves it to rest overnight. It is hand raised around a wooden die (mould) ready for the filling. Now, whereas several butchers may use left-overs or scraps for the fillings, Raymond will have none of that. His pork pie is made with freshly minced shoulder and seasonings, filled with his 'gravy' made in a huge saucepan from 'pig's feet, tails, bones, rind, ribs; anything to boil off for a jelly'. It costs £11.25.

He does not just stick to pork pies, branching out into all manner of fillings, each costing £16.75. Turkey, ham and cranberry has good chunks of both meats, with a refreshing contrast of the fruit; game is a coarse mix of rabbit, hare, pigeon, mallard, venison and wild boar stewed in red wine; and new this year is the pork, apple and Stilton, with its cubes of salty cheese and diced apple.

Labour Savers

Chesterton Farm Shop

Chesterton Lane, Cirencester, Gloucestershire, GL7 6JP

Tel: 01285 642160 Fax: 01285 653133

Contact: Gary Wallace. Last orders: 28 November. No credit cards. Delivery charge: next day delivery before 10 am, £20.27; before 1 pm, £13.22.

Two useful standbys for suppers over the Christmas break, that freeze well, come from the Chesterton Farm Shop using rare-breed primitive lamb. Saddle *en croute* is prepared from the eye fillet of the loin. Butcher Gary Wallace strips the loin (the piece weighs about 12 or 14oz), and wraps it in a hot water crust pastry. All you need do, once it is defrosted, is egg wash the pastry, bake it off in a hot oven for about 20 minutes, then cut it into slices and serve. Each saddle costs £8.50 a pound, and should feed three people generously.

Cushion of lamb is made from the boned shoulder. Stuffed with Gary's own-made stuffing of cranberries, orange and breadcrumbs, the shoulder is tied up like a plump cushion ready for roasting. These weigh around 4lb, cost £28 and feed six to eight people easily.

Heal Farm Meats

Kings Nympton, Umberleigh, Devon, EX37 9TB

Tel: 01769 574341 Fax: 01769 572839

Contact: Anne Petch. Last orders: 9 December. Switch, Delta, MasterCard, Visa. Delivery charge: prices include p&p.

If you have had a houseful over the holidays, by New Year's Eve you could be forgiven for never wanting to see the inside of a food shop or the outside of a stove again. Help is at hand in the form of a Heal Farm Dinner Party Kit. It will save you from the horrors of the former and, I am assured, cut down the time spent in the kitchen considerably.

A kit comes complete with all the main ingredients needed – but no vegetables – so you can (and here I quote from the publicity blurb) 'prepare a thoroughly delicious meal for six people'. On offer for this New Year's Eve – or for any night if it comes to that – is a rillette of smoked trout, a choice of cubed shoulder of venison in port or boned saddle of Shetland lamb with a ginger and hazelnut stuffing, damson fruit cheese with Greek yoghurt, and a hefty slice of Devon Garland cheese with Orkney oatcakes.

Everything is either ready to serve or fully prepared and ready to cook, is made by Heal Farm or comes from various small speciality producers, and is suitable for freezing. A kit serves six people and costs £60 including delivery. Even my rudimentary maths can grasp that it costs £10 a head. And if it saves you hassle, time and worry, it seems a reasonable price to pay.

The Scottish Gourmet
Thistle Mill, Biggar, Strathclyde, ML12 6LP
Tel: 01899 221268 Fax: 01899 220456
Contact: Gillian Bell. Last orders: 8 December. Switch, MasterCard, Visa, Amex, Diners. Delivery charge: £6.85; over eight items, p&p free.

A source of great convenience, the Scottish Gourmet tries hard to cater for your every need. A browse through their brochure whets the appetite and would inspire anyone to entertain over the holidays, especially when everything arrives ready to go.

Christmas pie would go down a treat on Boxing Day. Made with chunks of Red deer from the Highlands, beef and goose from Aberdeenshire and game from the Borders, it is gently stewed with mushrooms, onions, carrots and celery, air-dried ham, Port and Madeira. The filling and puff-pastry lid arrive together, so all you need do is put the filling into an oven-proof pie dish, close the lid and cook for about half an hour. Prices start at £8.87 to serve two, and go up to £23.67 which is enough for six. There are several other ready-cooked casseroles and stews, such as the Lamington made with pheasant from the near-by Lamington estate. In fact you could almost manage the entire holiday without rousing yourself to do anything more than turning on the oven or microwave for a quick reheat.

Shopping delivered
I may well be in a minority of one but I rarely – if ever – venture into a supermarket unless it is to stock up on washing powder, loo paper and others of life's essentials. But there are millions who do, and who constantly moan at the checkout queues during the build-up to Christmas.

For those who live in central London, help is at hand in the form of the Food Ferry, 31 Glycena Road, London, SW11 5TP (Tel: 0171 498 0827, Fax: 0171 498 8009, email HYPERLINK mailto:foodferry @corporate.nethead.co.uk). With a minimum order of £20 and a fixed delivery charge of £3.50, they will shop for you. They send out a catalogue listing over 2,200 items of branded goods (they are not too keen on own-label supermarket brands), but apart from Fairy washing-up liquid or Kleenex, you can order up fresh vegetables, ready-to-go foods prepared by the Pie Man, even your turkey and Christmas pudding. And yes, they will even deliver on Christmas Eve.

Flanagan's Supermarket Direct, Flanagan House, 118–120 Garratt Lane, London, SW18 4DJ (Tel: 0181 877 8000, Fax: 0181 877 8020) offers a similar service, currently in London only, although it plans to go nationwide. With a £4 delivery charge, it offers discounts with a privilege card for shoppers, and a full range of own-label and branded goods. Either way, these seem an extremely good idea. Now I need never go into a supermarket again.

Christmas Treats From Around The World

Betty's by Post

1 Parliament Street, Harrogate, Yorkshire, HG1 2QU
Tel: 01423 886055 Fax: 01423 881083
Contact: Fiona Hunter. Visa. Last orders: 5 December. No credit cards.
Delivery charge: £5.50 p&p.

In Yorkshire, Betty's Tea Rooms are an institution. Whether it is for a cup of tea and a fat rascal (a cross between a rock cake and a scone which hails from the Moors), or just a loaf of wholemeal bread, who can resist popping in? And if you are wondering why such an apparently English institution features in 'Treats From Around the World', you should know that Betty's was founded by Frederick Belmont, a Swiss confectioner. It remains a family firm and they still return regularly to Switzerland bringing back all manner of baked specialities from Germany, Austria and Italy as well as Switzerland to inspire the bakery.

Betty's By Post is their mail-order arm, set up to deliver anywhere in the country. Everything is made in small batches in their bakery using the best ingredients (butter, fresh cream and unbleached white flour). Of course they do make Christmas puddings and cakes – and very good they are too – but I want to concentrate on the foreign.

Biber – a Christmas biscuit from Switzerland – is made with ground roasted almonds and hazelnuts bound together with honey and spiced with cinnamon and a dash of Kirsch. It makes for an incredibly chewy, moist texture with a full flavour of nuts, and comes in various shapes and sizes. A *biber* fairy or drummer boy costs £2.45, a tiny *biber* wreath decorated with split almonds, 'natural' cherries and green icing holly leaves costs £2.10, and the traditional *biber* round, a large biscuit about 5 inches in diameter and decorated with flourishes of icing sugar, split almonds and cherries, costs £5.75.

Betty's is proud of its *Lebkuchen* (gingerbread), and understandably so. Made from black treacle, golden syrup, cinnamon, nutmeg, ground ginger and mixed spices, it is crisp to the bite and quietly fiery. Again this is made in all sorts of shapes and sizes. Tree hangings, complete with a ribbon threaded through for hanging on the tree, cost £6.25 for a pack of ten that include stars, trees, hearts and angels. There is an 8-inch tree-shaped biscuit covered with an almond paste and decorated with glacé figs, angelica and cherries, and a cut-out snowman, rocking horse or stocking, coloured red with dyed kernal (apricot) paste. And although they do make proper stand-up gingerbread houses, they will not send these by post.

New this year is *panforte bianco*, costing £6.98, which I have to say is not actually white, rather orangey-yellow like a rich sponge cake. Made with ground almonds, orange, lemon and citron peel, honey, marzipan, orange flower water and orange oil, its texture is unlike most panforte in that it is moister, less chewy and less nutty. But what it does have going for it is the strong flavour of orange flowers that reverberates on (see also Mortimer and Bennett, page 167). Betty's also make *stollen*, *panettone* and Austrian *Linzer* cake.

Carluccio's

28a Neal Street, London, WC2H 9PS

Tel: 0171 240 1487 Fax: 0171 497 1361

email: carluccios@cix.compulink.co.uk

Contact: Bob Hamilton. Last orders: 15 December. Switch, MasterCard, Visa, Amex.Delivery charge: p&p extra.

Carluccio's is the shop belonging to Italian TV chef Antonio Carluccio and his wife Priscilla. Together they have developed a range of foods, either own-made or imported from Italy. Everything is superbly packaged (Priscilla is a Conran, and knows about these things.) But I have to warn you that prices tend to be a little on the high side.

Panettone comes in a choice of *Tradizionale* and Cappuccino, costing around £14.25 and £14.95. Rather more modest is the *pan pepato* (literally pepper bread) costing £3.50 for 100g. This is a different style of *panforte* (see page 157), made with toasted nuts, candied water melon and orange, honey and flour, and coated with a mixture of pepper, nutmeg, cinnamon and various other spices. Soft and relatively crumbly to eat, it has a pronounced pepperiness that just lifts the flavour and warms the mouth.

The Caviar House

161 Piccadilly, London, W1V 9DF

Tel: 0171 409 0445 Fax: 0171 493 1667

Contact: Susie Boeckmann. Last orders: 12 December. Switch, Delta, MasterCard, Visa, Amex, Diners. Delivery charge: p&p extra.

When it comes to treats, caviar must be *le dernier cri*. I make no claims to be an expert, because sadly I have not eaten it often enough to really know the best. But when I do, I adore it. Of course it might just be the sheer wicked indulgence of knowing I am eating something extravagantly expensive, but I think not. It is heaven: tiny, shiny, silky balls that explode in the mouth releasing the savours of sea breeze and subtle salt.

Fellow food writer Ian Wisniewski knows all about caviar. As he explains: 'It is the female sturgeon's roe we have to thank for it, and while there are some 20 varieties of sturgeon, the three that really count are Beluga, Oscietre and Sevruga; all natives of the Caspian sea. Fisherman should not be interested in sturgeon until they're mature enough to spawn, which means at least seven years old in the case of Sevruga, 12 to 15 for the Oscietre, and 22 to 25 for the Beluga. Once netted, they're washed and opened by hand on marble slabs. The eggs are then pushed through a coarse sieve to remove any membranes, before being sampled, appraised and preserved through salting. The amount of salt added is crucial. Too little and the caviar will perish; too much and it will dry up.

'Beluga, with its large "fragile" eggs varying in colour from light to dark grey that yield a distinctive nutty taste, is undoubtedly the rarest and most expensive of the caviars. The general consensus, however, is that Oscietre usually offers the finest quality; its eggs are only slightly smaller, ranging from dark black to golden brown with a subtle creamy flavour. And that leaves Sevruga with the unfortunate association of being the cheapest. Its eggs are the smallest of all three, with a grey to mid-brown colouring and a delightful sea-salt flavour.'

When it comes to choosing caviar, it is not only the different types of roe that are debated but also where it comes from: Iran or Russia. Most of what is imported is Iranian, and it is nowadays generally considered better quality with better defined grains. Standards have dropped in the Russian republics since caviar production stopped being centrally controlled from Moscow.

The Caviar House is a reliable source. A 50g portion of Beluga costs £101; 50g of Oscietre, £48 and 50g of Sevruga £36. And as they say, caviar has two enemies: air and heat. So serve it over crushed ice, and never expose it to the air for longer than an hour. As for what to eat it with, forget about all those fancy trimmings and chilled vodka. Champagne, some good French bread and unsalted butter will do very nicely.

The Clark Trading Company
Freepost (Lon1083), London, SE12 8BR
Tel: 0181 297 9937 Fax: 0181 297 9993
Contact: Colin Clark. Last orders: 15 December. Switch, Delta, MasterCard, Visa. Delivery charge: £3.95; for orders over £75, carriage free.

All over Spain you can find *turron* (nougat). If you ask any Spaniard where to buy the best, he almost always answers Alicante. Quite why, I am not sure: perhaps it is because they use their local bitter-sweet almonds and perfumed honey, but I must admit that when I sampled the Alicante product I found myself agreeing. The Clark Trading Company imports four different *turrons* from Alicante. New this year is the soft, chewier and sticker *turron* that you either love or hate depending on the state of your teeth. The other three are all hard and brittle. Generously full of nuts, these come as *tortas imperiales*, a thin round *turron* weighing 200g and costing £4.50; the block-shaped *turron Alicante*; and *turron de chocolate* weighing 300g and costing £5.75. This, I have to say, I found the least successful of all. The chocolate detracts, rather than adds, to the satisfying combination of egg whites, nuts, sugar and honey that makes turron the indulgence it is.

Membrillo is Spanish for quince, but also means a thick fruity quince paste. This is one of the components that make up the 12-fruits desserts served over Christmas in several Mediterranean countries. Made with just quince and sugar, it is quite solid in texture so it can be cut into cubes, and comes in a 300g tube at £2.75.

Conservas Rainha Santa

Old Spitalfields Market, 49 Brushfield Street, London, E1 6AA

Tel: 0171 247 2802 Fax: 0171 247 2802

Contact: Timothy Clements. Last orders: 17 December. No credit cards. Delivery charge: £2.95 p&p.

Elvas plums from Portugal are truly one of Christmas's luxuries. Little pale green jewels made from the greengage, they are sweet, succulent and very meaty. Once the greengages are picked around the third week in July, the laborious process of preserving them begins. First the fruit is carefully blanched and cooked at least four times in a sugar syrup, then left to stand in the syrup for about six weeks. Finally it is washed in water and left to dry in the sun before it is stored away for Christmas. All this meticulous work is carried out in order to achieve just the right taste and consistency. A good Elvas plum must be sweet but not so much so that it drowns the inherent flavour of the fruit. When you pick one up, it must not be too sticky or sugary so it sticks to the fingers. It must be soft – but not so soft that it disintegrates at first bite – and it must be juicy. The Portuguese are very particular, and would frown on any Elvas plums that are so juicy that they dribble down the face. Conserva Rainha Santa imports very superior Elvas plums packed in the traditional wooden boxes. A 250g box contains ten Elvas plums and costs £8; or if you prefer you can buy a mixed box of plums with figs and apricots for £9.50.

The Deli at Cooksbridge

Station House, Cooksbridge, Lewes, Sussex, BN8 4SW

Tel: 01273 401287 Fax: 01273 401740

Contact: Peter Bromwich. Last orders: 16 December. Switch, Delta, MasterCard, Visa. Delivery charge: £3.50 p&p up to 1kg.

Peter Bromwich of The Deli imports duck foie gras direct from south-west France. Jealously guarding the actual name and location of his sources, he buys 'on quality' direct from three or four trusted producers. It comes from Barbary and Rouen ducks that nowadays are force fed only for about three weeks and on a corn liquid. And, according to Peter, even though the French have made foie gras their own, it originates from Hungary where it was produced by Jewish gypsies.

When choosing foie gras he looks for a 'solid, rock hard texture, a light yellow, what I think of as a mousy hair colour, with a pinkness in the middle. Then I check for how much work has been involved in its preparation or its veining. I buy when it has been de-veined from the exterior, not into the lobes as they can get bruised, with the least amount of work possible for the best possible quality of extra cru: the top grade.'

Peter sells his foie gras as whole raw lobes that weigh between 550 and 750g and cost around £36 per kg (it is difficult to fix the actual price until nearer Christmas). These come vacuum packed, and are for pan-frying or however you like to cook them. He produces his own *entier* from whole pieces of the liver that are first marinaded in port and bas-Armagnac, then cooked in jars in their own fat with a fresh bay leaf studded with a clove. A sealed jar weighing 150g costs £23.50, and a 300g jar is £47.

He also makes a parfait which he describes as 'in a country style, not so silky smooth that it is a mousse, and still with some texture and bite'. This time the livers are marinaded in Madeira and bas-Armagnac, then cooked with shallots, fresh thyme, pasteurised egg, unsalted butter and a minimum amount of chicken livers, and finally puréed and sieved. It is sold vacuum packed by weight, and costs £40 per kilo.

Peter also imports *bloc* from south-west France in jars costing £4.40 for 50g for duck liver, £5.40 for goose liver (this is the only goose liver product he handles, on the grounds that goose liver is 'horrendously expensive and very few – if any – can tell the difference between the two'). Now in case you do not know what *bloc* is (and until I talked to Peter I must admit I was not too sure), it is a mousse made not only with the foie gras but also the rest of the offal (gizzards and so on) that are ground up and pressed, which is why – comparatively speaking – it works out cheaper.

Extraco

29 Parkwood Road, London, SW19 7AQ

Tel: 0181 944 1385 Fax: 0181 944 1385

Contact: Diana Campbell-Smith. Last orders: 15 December. No credit cards.

Delivery charge: up to 500g, £2.10; 1kg, £3.50; 2kg, £4.10; 3kg, £4.70; 4kg, £5.25; 5kg, £5.70.

The Greeks are notorious for their love of sweet things, so it comes as no surprise that at Christmas they celebrate by indulging their sweet teeth. *Kourabiedes*, loosely translated as almond shortbreads, are three-bite-size crescent-shaped biscuits made with flour, sugar, butter, egg and whole and ground almonds. With a short crumbly texture and covered in icing sugar, they are traditional at this time of year, and a 200g box containing about six to seven biscuits costs £3.75.

Melomakarona is a moist, syrupy, honey and walnut cake spiced with cloves, nutmeg and cinnamon and made with olive oil rather than butter. Sold as individual three-bite size cakes, they are what the Greeks refer to as *politika*, meaning a food originating from Constantinople when it was under Greek rule and tending to sweetness or spiciness. *Loukoumia* (Turkish – or should I say Greek? – delight) also fits that category. Now made in Salonika, the 400g boxes costing £3.80 come in a choice of two flavours, heavily scented rose or almond, generously dusted with icing sugar and complete with a small wooden fork. *Mandoles*, whole roasted caramelised almonds dipped in dark chocolate, are another treat; and although *koufeta*, sugared almonds, are for weddings and christenings, they are popular at Christmas as well. All these and many more Greek treats are imported by Extraco.

Jeroboams
96 Holland Park Avenue, London W11 3RB
Tel: 0171 727 9359 Fax: 0171 792 9792 email: cheese@jeroboams.co.uk
Contact: Clare Rich. Last orders: 13 December. Switch, Delta, MasterCard, Visa, Amex, Diners. Delivery charge: £3.95.

Vacherin Mont d'Or is described by Patrick Rance in *The French Cheese Book* (Macmillan) as a 'succulent seasonal cheese of such glory that it has become the solace of our winter months'. There are two versions, one made in Switzerland and the other in the Franche-Comté in France, and it is the latter that Jereboams sell, costing £22.50 for a 1½lb cheese, with a packet of Fudge's Bakery digestive biscuits.

Traditionally made from the unpasteurised milk from MontbÈliard and red and white cows grazing in the French Alps at an altitude higher than 700 metres, Vacherin Mont d'Or is produced only from early autumn until the end of the winter. The rest of the year the milk is used for Comté cheese. The process of making Vacherin Mont d'Or is unique. 'Once the curds are removed from the mould,' explains Patrick Rance, 'they are ringed with spruce bark. The bark becomes attached to the outside of the cheese and its resinous savour and aroma gradually penetrate inside the soft white pâté, which becomes meltingly soft as it comes to full maturity.' The mature cheese is packed in a pine box, and to eat it you carefully remove the wrinkled yellow to pinkish gold crust and spoon out the soft inside. As it ripens and matures, it grows even runnier and more liquid.

Konditor & Cook
22 Cornwall Road, London, SE1 8TW
Tel: 0171 261 0456 Fax: 0171 261 9021
Contact: Gerhard Jenne. Last orders: 12 December. Switch, MasterCard, Visa. Delivery charge: p&p extra.

German master baker Gerhard Jenne of Konditor & Cook once worked at Konditorei Kreutzkamm, the famous pastry shop in Munich. Now safely installed in London in a tiny shop with a bakery attached, he bakes all sorts of his country's specialities for Christmas.

Everything is made with quality ingredients – butter, free-range eggs and plump fruit – on a small scale, and there is a freshness and vibrancy of flavour in his products. *Stollen*, described by Gerhard as 'a brioche with sultanas soaked in rum, mixed peel and flaked almonds in the dough, with a wedge of own-made marzipan with brandy through the centre', is baked no earlier than November to ensure its freshness. Apparently in Germany they actually like it dry, whereas we prefer it moist. Dipped in butter and rolled in castor sugar when it comes out of the oven, 'to form a shell while it is still hot', it is then sprinkled with icing sugar. Eat it thinly sliced for a 'melt-on-the tongue' sensation. One weighing 500g costs £6.25, and 1kg costs £11.45.

Zimtsterne – cinnamon and almond stars – are a flour-free Christmas cookie. Similar in texture to a macaroon, they are made with whipped egg white, cinnamon and almonds cut into little stars about 1½ inches across. Hard on the outside but gloriously gooey inside, they are sold loose or in packs of seven costing, at last year's price, £2.75. Also worth a bite and on sale throughout the year are the black and white sables. Easily recognisable by the twirl effect from the chocolate and vanilla, they are very buttery and, Gerhard claims, 'the nearest thing to shortbread'.

Korona Delicatessen

30 Streatham High Road, Streatham, London, SW16 1BZ

Tel: 0181 769 6647

Contact: Eleanor Wicinska. Last orders: 10 December. No credit cards.

Delivery charge: p&p extra.

Christmas Eve, in Poland, is celebrated with a vast meal of 12 meatless dishes. These, so Eleanor Wicinska tells me, include *pierogi*, the Polish answer to ravioli stuffed with wild mushrooms, *uszka* (tortelloni), sauerkraut with yet more wild mushrooms, stuffed cabbage and carp. Whilst Eleanor does sell these, either imported from Poland or made by various Polish ladies in their kitchens over here, for obvious reasons she will not send them by mail.

What she will send out, however, are pickled *sledzi* (herrings), whole moist *makowic* (poppy seed cake) or *piernik* (honey cake) weighing 1½lb and costing £2.65. If you fancy making your own, she has any-sized tubs of ready-prepared poppy seed paste. Another speciality on Christmas Eve is dried-fruit compôte made with, amongst other things, *sliwki wedzone* (smoked prunes). A 250g packet costs £1.68, and if you do use them I would love to know what they taste like. Something I do indulge in most years are *sliwki w czekoladic* (chocolate-coated prunes). These are (plain) prunes soaked in a vanilla-flavoured liqueur and coated in chocolate. Meaty and bitter-sweet, a ½lb box costs £4.15, and make a most unusual sweetmeat.

La Fromagerie

30 Highbury Park, Highbury, London, N5 2AA
Tel: 0171 359 7440 Fax: 0171 359 7440
Contact: Patricia Michelson. Last orders: 7 December. Switch, Delta, MasterCard, Visa, Amex. Delivery charge: p&p extra.

La Fromagerie imports an interesting selection of Italian sweetmeats (dried or crystallised fruits) for Christmas. From Padua come truly memorable quartered clementines dipped in a dark chocolate and individually wrapped in a 400g box costing £13.85. Clementines from Puglia are sold loose, costing £3.95 for 113g. These are lightly crystallised in a loose sugar fondant, and when you bite into them they are wonderfully juicy. Fig balls, the size of a cricket ball, are made from dark figs gently dried and wrapped up in vine leaves. Sweet, chewy and recommended to go with Stilton, they come from Calabria and cost £4.45 for 250g.

A small family company in Bari, serviced by various deftly fingered aunts, uncles and cousins, is the source of little treats, all charmingly individually wrapped in various coloured papers, and costing £3.95 for 113g. There are fresh chestnuts dipped in chocolate, dates stuffed with walnuts, chocolate apricots or figs, or fresh blueberries and redcurrants stuck together with chocolate to look like florentines. These 'parcels' can be tied to a tree, or mixed in a bowl with other fruits and nuts for an eye-catching centrepiece.

Larsen Wines

6 Eggars Hill, Aldershot, Hampshire, GU11 3NQ
Tel: 01252 334499 Fax: 01252 334490 email: larson@larson.co.uk
Contact: Birte Nielsen. Last orders: 15 December. Switch, Delta, MasterCard, Visa, Amex. Delivery charge: £1 p&p.

In Denmark, the first Sunday of Advent sees the start of the run-up to Christmas. The Danes light a single Advent candle (the following Sunday they light two, and so on until all four candles are alight on the last Sunday), and drink their first glass of mulled wine. Now you may have made mulled wine by mixing your own spices or buying ready-mixed packets, but I assure you that Danish mulled wine is very different. There they use gløgg, a 50-per-cent-proof white alcohol infused with such spices as cinnamon and cloves. Open a bottle, and one whiff will convince you of its strength, so you will need no more than a half a teaspoon for every glass. It is imported by Larsen Wines, and sold in 50ml bottles costing £2.95. One bottle of gløgg is enough to spice up four bottles of wine. Traditionally the Danes add sultanas and slithers of blanched almonds to red wine while it is heating, then serve it with a spoon.

Rumour has it that Larsen Wines also intend to import an

œbleskiver pan this year. For the uninitiated, *œbleskiver* are small balls of a light batter similar to a doughnut. You cook them on top of the stove in a specially shaped heavy pan, then serve them while still warm, sprinkled with icing sugar, with a bowl of strawberry jam and a glass of mulled wine.

The Little Red Barn

New Timber Lodge, Silchester, Berkshire, RG7 2PN

Tel: 0118 971 4515 Fax: 0118 971 4322 email: redbarn@dial.pipex.com
Contact: Adriana Rabinovich .Last orders: 15 December. Switch, Delta,MasterCard, Visa. Delivery charge: up to 1kg, £3.75; 1–2kg, £6.75; 2–3kg, £8.50.

'A good brownie,' says Adriana Rabinovich of the Little Red Barn, 'needs to be home made. You have to cook them in small batches as it is the only way to get it right.' And if you are wondering what a 'right' brownie is like, according to Adriana 'it must be very chewy, very chocolatey. Moist in the centre with a crispy top.'

She comes from Philadelphia, where they obviously know their brownies. Using the family's recipes that have been 'improved' over generations, she has built up a small but successful business making all things American: cookies, barn nuts (caramelised almonds and pecans), prairie mix (toasted and spiced pretzels, peanuts and Shreddies) and, of course, brownies. Favourite is the fudgey-textured double chocolate, made with butter, sugar, eggs, flour and chocolate. The choice of chocolate is all-important. In the USA they use a baker's unsweetened chocolate, over here Andrea uses a Belgian version which she assures me is 'just as good – if not better.' Her brownies really are terribly good. As I write, I am ploughing my way through a packet and the texture is certainly as Andrea describes it: the crunch on top, the silkiness of the centre and the crisp bite as your teeth hit a chocolate chunk. As for the taste, it's not too sweet nor too sickly, and with a dark chocolate richness.

On a more seasonal note, Andrea tells me that serious fans serve the Cherry Bourbon Pecan Brownies instead of Christmas pudding. Moist, very fruity (they contain bitter-sweet cherries and pecans), and laced with alcohol, I can quite understand why. A 850g tray that cuts up into 20 brownies would be just the thing. Otherwise they are sent in 200g cellophane packs, with prices around £3.99.

Machiavelli
83 Kinnerton Street, London, SW1X 8ED
Tel: 0171 259 5761 Fax: 0171 259 5780
Contact: Ninai Zarach. Last orders: 12 December. No credit cards. Delivery charge: p&p extra.

At Christmas, Florentines tuck into a Pecorino cheese with truffles, or so Ninai Zarach assures me. But as it is so heavenly I cannot see why they do not eat it all year round.

Sold as a relatively young Pecorino – no more than two months – it is still fairly soft to cut, with a creamy freshness. But it is the truffles, the tiny grated specks of pungent wonderfulness, that make all the difference. They transform the cheese from the ordinary to the extraordinary, lifting it with their pungent aroma of veiled muskiness. A 600g cheese costs £20, and comes vacuum-packed and in a split-wooden basket.

Maison Blanc
37 St John's Wood High Street, London, NW8 7NJ
Tel: 0171 586 1982 Fax: 0171 586 1087
Contact: Mandy Kenyon. Last orders: 22 December. Switch, Delta, MasterCard, Visa, Diners. Personal shoppers only.

If we like to stuff ourselves with Christmas pudding, the French prefer to pick at a *buche de Noel*. Log-shaped and often decorated with holly, meringue-shaped mushrooms, elves, leaves and other flights of woodland fantasy, the base is usually a sponge roulade with layers of butter cream spread in and over. Such a fragile cake is, understandably, hard to deliver, so if you want to indulge you will have to collect it personally.

Maison Blanc produce four highly decorated and innovative versions. These include *crème au beurre chocolat*, which has a biscuit base, a chocolate sponge roulade with chocolate butter cream, and somewhat unseasonal raspberries. The top is crammed with fir trees and snowmen, and the sides dragged with a fork for the proper bark effect. *Larieux* is far more rich and sophisticated, with its smooth chocolate glaze covering a chocolate and almond base interleaved with layers of dark and milk chocolate mousse. Prices start at £8.50. And as they are made freshly on a daily basis, apparently you can leave it until two days before Christmas before you place an order.

Mortimer and Bennett

33 Turnham Green Terrace, Chiswick, London, W4 1RG

Tel: 0181 995 4145 Fax: 0181 742 3068

Contacts: Dan Mortimer and Di Bennett. Last orders: 12 December. Switch, Delta, MasterCard, Visa, Amex. Delivery charge: extra by weight.

Although no more than a tiny shop, Mortimer and Bennett imports several fine 'Treats from Abroad'. They sell an exceptionally good *panforte* from Marabisi, an artisinal baker with branches in and around Sienna. If once *panforte*, a speciality from Sienna made from dried fruit and nuts pressed into a round 'cake', was seasonal to Christmas, it is now so much in demand by tourists that it is made all year round. Margherita – the most usual variety – is made with almonds, sugar, candied orange and lemon peel and honey and a dusting of white icing sugar. Unlike several I have tried, there is no skimping of the ingredients here. It is jammed full of whole nuts and large chunks of the peel. Nero is a darker, bitterer version, no doubt from the addition of the cocoa powder. I find this takes away from the intrinsic flavour of the fruits. Unquestionably my favourite is the *pan pepato*, with its almonds, candied melon, honey and various spices including, I think, cumin. And I am much impressed by its deep medieval richness and firm but chewy texture. All three come in 250g and 500g packs, and cost £5.95 and £8.95 respectively.

Also made by Marabisi are *panettone* and *pandoro*, both at £10.95. *Panettone*, a light, fragile cake studded with sultanas and candied peel, sold in distinctive cardboard boxes, is by now familiar to most of us. *Pandoro* (golden bread), relatively new to Britain, is another matter. I have not tried it but food writer Philippa Davenport was much impressed. '[It] is an ethereal high-rise, star-shaped cake with an egg and butter-soft crumb unspotted by so much as a single sultana or nugget of candied peel. It is by virtue of its purity, more digestible than panettone.... The best brands are distinctly buttery, yet light. *Pandoro* is sold complete with a sachet of vanilla-flavoured icing sugar to shake over the cake just before serving, a snowstorm of added fun.'

Kreutzkamm, with branches in Dresden and Munich, is another small craft bakery with very high standards. From them Mortimer and Bennett buy *Ingwar Küchen* (Christmas ginger bread) and *Kriststollen* costing £12.95 for 700g and £15.95 for 1kg. Rich in butter, this version of the heavily fruited yeast cake is unusual in that, unlike most, it has no marzipan running through the centre.

The Oil Merchant
47 Ashchurch Grove, London, W12 9BU
Tel: 0181 740 1335 Fax: 0181 740 1319
email: The_Oil_Merchant@compuserve.com
Contact: Sika Carey. No credit cards. Delivery charge: £3 for orders under £25; otherwise free.

Marrons glacés (candied chestnuts) come from the sweet rather than the horse chestnut tree. Apparently an old Italian law stipulates that only plump and round marrons grown in three areas – the Piedmont , the Apennine Mountains and Lazio – can be used for this glorious sweetmeat. Agrimontana, a northern Italian company, produces some of the very best, fat, velvety-smooth marrons I have ever tasted.

Like Elvas plums (see page 160), to make them takes time, effort and care. Once the marrons are harvested between October and December, they are left to soak in great tubs of water where they start fermenting. This not only stabilises the fruit but also allows it to take up the glacé more easily. They are dried and laid out on racks in caves near Rome for 30 days where they are turned regularly with a wooden tong-like instrument to avoid bruising. Then modern technology comes into play as the marrons are taken to the factory near Bologna, where they are steam-peeled (so as not to burn them) and glacéed by gentle poaching in a sugar syrup. They are very lush, very meaty and to be savoured over the holidays.

The Pastry Shop
56 New Cavendish Street, London, W1M 7LE
Tel: 0171 935 0188 Fax: 0171 935 0188
Contact: Mark Peregrine. Last orders: 13 December. No credit cards. Delivery charge: p&p extra.

The Pastry Shop opened just before Christmas 1996, run by Mark Peregrine and his wife Maryanne. Everything is freshly made on the premises to exceptionally high standards. Mark's training has been impeccable. 'A chef at heart', he has worked in the kitchens of such luminaries as Raymond Blanc, Marc Meneau of L'Esperance ('where I was shoved on to the pastry section and fell in love with it') and Louis Outhier of L'Oasis.

Now that he is able to give full rein to his love for pastry, you will find at Christmas time splendid *buches de Nöel*, decorated in the French-style with mushroom-shaped meringues. Another fantasy is the *croque-en-bouche*, really more for weddings. Mark seasonally dresses his pastry cream-stuffed choux buns into a foot and half high pyramid on a nougatine base, dribbles caramel over them and dots little edible gold balls for a 'Christmas tree effect'. This confection, enough for 12 to 15 portions, costs £25 but cannot, as I am sure you will understand, be delivered by mail.

What he is prepared to send is his astoundingly light and fluffy brioche. In France this is often served thinly sliced and lightly toasted with foie gras (see The Deli at Cooksbridge, page 160, and R E Campbell, below) over the holidays, although Mark also recommends it with smoked salmon. Made with eggs, butter, flour and yeast, the 1lb loaf costs £9 and is made exactly how he likes them. That is to say, 'with a good brown crust, a rich yellow colour interior; I like colour and I don't like pale brioches. And they have a good taste of butter and beautiful aeration'. As Mark also likes his brioche cut thickly, he reckons a loaf will cut into eight slices, but I would have thought that might be erring on the side of caution.

R E Campbell Ltd

69 Maltings Place, Bagley's Lane, London, SW6 2BY

Tel: 0171 371 5566 Fax: 0171 371 5676

Contact: Bob Campbell. Last orders: 16 December. No credit cards. Delivery charge: £8 minimum charge.

I think we should get one thing straight. If the *gavage* (cramming) of geese to fatten their livers for foie gras distresses you, then you have a choice. Either do as Bob Campbell does and do not think about it, or do not eat it. Nobody in their right mind welcomes such treatment of animals but, as Bob says, 'the pleasure of eating foie gras is so immense, I don't dwell on how it got on my plate'.

Bob has been dwelling in the luxury end of the food market – caviar, foie gras, smoked salmon and truffles – for several years and numbers among his clients the Savoy, the Dorchester and the Connaught hotels. His foie gras is imported from Strasbourg from one of the few remaining family businesses, and he sells it both from duck and geese. And unlike Peter Bromwich (see page 160) he definitely can tell the difference between the two. 'Goose is smoother and sweeter, whereas duck is more robust. If you like the flavour of wild duck – its gaminess – then duck is the one you should go for.'

Peter's preference is for goose foie gras and this he keeps in various forms. It comes as whole raw intact livers for sautéing, pan-frying or terrines, which he supplies (and only to personal shoppers or by delivery in London only) in 1kg packs that will set you back £50 for goose and £35 for duck.

In the *mi-cuit* (cooked but still pink) range there are several stunners that make a very fancy first course. Christmas *croûte*, a whole cooked foie gras studded with truffles and wrapped in a highly decorated pastry case, comes in a whole range of weights. The lightest, 355g, costs £70 and should feed seven comfortably. Also enough for seven is whole liver, again truffled, set in Madeira aspic in a crock, costing £66.27 for 325g. And there are *torchons* (meaning cloth), where the foie gras is gently cooked wrapped in a tea towel to form a sort of sausage-shape; and here Bob recommends the duck as being vastly superior.

At the more affordable end of the market, Bob has a *bocal* at £16.41 for 150g of whole foie gras in Madeira jelly in a glass jar, or a 330g tin of purée made from 55-per-cent goose liver with goose fat and poultry liver costing £6. With seemingly dozens of foie gras products for both the aficionado or the first timer, he will happily discuss any order to make sure it fits the bill.

Taste of the Wild

31 London Stone Estate, Broughton Street, London, SW8 3QJ

Tel: 0171 498 5654 Fax: 0171 498 5419

Contact: Alistair Lomax. Last orders: 19 December. MasterCard, Visa, Amex, Diners. Delivery charge: carriage free for orders in Central London and over £100; otherwise £10 per order; minimum order £20.

In the normal course of events chocolate truffles do not contain truffles. They get their name from their look rather than their taste. Urbani, a long-established Italian truffle company, have gone one better: they now make a real chocolate truffle – or perhaps I should say a two bite-size truffle – that contains specks of the powerful *Tuber aestivum* (black summer truffle). Specks, in this case, however are more than enough to perfume the chocolate. Each one comes in an individual packet, and as soon as you tear it open your nose starts twitching. Did I like it? Well I am not totally sure whether I would have rather had the truffle and the chocolate separately, but it is certainly a new, indulgent taste sensation. Imported by Taste of the Wild, a box of 18 chocolate truffles costs £6.

The Teesdale Trencherman

Startforth Hall, Barnard Castle, Co Durham, DL12 9RA

Tel: 01833 638370 Fax: 01833 631218

Contact: Johnny Cooke-Hurle. Last orders: 11 December. MasterCard, Visa. Delivery charge: up to 1lb, £2.50; 1–2lb, £3.60; 2–3 lb, £4.95; over 3lb, £6.

Drowned in marsala, for a sensational alcoholic haze, is a *Veneziana farcita*. A moist sponge cake with a layer of zabaglione running through its centre, this Italian speciality is made by master baker Severo Marcanato just outside Venice. Light, fluffy and wonderfully rich, it knocks the spots off a panettone (see Mortimer and Bennett, page 167). A 500g cake, attractively wrapped in bright orange and red glossy paper tied up with gold string, costs £6.50 and can be mailed by the Teesdale Trencherman. Failing that, ring the importers, the Merchant Gourmet on 0345 585168, and they will give you details of your nearest stockist.

Presents For Food Lovers

Starting in October and through until December there are literally hundreds of Christmas fairs all over the country. Many of them are held in aid of charities but some are commercially run. Several friends do all their Christmas shopping at them, and have a splendid day out into the bargain. What is on offer obviously varies from fair to fair, but you can usually rely on finding unusual, often hand-made goodies from the smaller producer. Some of the best fairs are:

8–9 October: The Asthma Fair, The Hurlingham Club, London SW6 (contact: Dawn Caroe, Tel: 0171 602 6982)

4–6 November: Irnham Hall, Lincolnshire (contact: Lady Benton Jones, Tel: 01476 550212)

6 November: Duntreath Castle, north of Glasgow (contact: Lady Edmonstone, Tel: 01360 770215)

10–11 November: Macmillan Cancer Fund Christmas Market, Royal Horticultural Hall, Vincent Square, London SW1 (contact: Katherine O'Kelly, Tel: 0171 795 0055)

29–30 November: Presents Galore, Rowley Mile Racecourse, Newmarket (contact: Wendy Millbank, Tel: 01638 668802)

Mary Howard (Tel: 01386 700850) runs three fairs each year. This year they are on 30–31 October at York Racecourse, 13–14 November at Ascot Racecourse and 20–21 November at Hullavington Barracks, near Chippenham, Wiltshire.

Presents under £5

America Direct

85 Woodside Avenue, London N10 3HF

Tel: 0181 365 2544 Fax: 0181 365 2820

Last orders: 12 December. Switch, Delta, MasterCard, Visa. Delivery charge: on orders under £25, £2.50; £25–75, £3.50; over £75, p&p free.

America Direct stocks all sorts of goodies imported from the USA. If you like – or have never even tried – pretzels, you have a treat in store. Harry's pretzels really are good: hard, crunchy and properly salted. There are two varieties, plain Sourdough or Everything, where the pretzels are covered in poppy seeds, sesame seeds, onion, garlic and salt. A 400g bag costs £2.95, and will tuck snugly into a stocking.

Anything Left-Handed Ltd

57 Brewer Street, London W1R 3FB

Tel: 0181 770 3722 Fax: 0181 715 1220

MasterCard, Visa. Last orders: 15 December. No credit cards. Delivery charge: £1 p&p for orders up to £7.50; over £7.50, £2.

One of my best friends is left-handed. She is always complaining about how difficult it makes her life, so each Christmas I try to find her a really useful gadget. For a left-hander, cutting with a right-handed serrated knife is a particular problem as it makes a curved cut. This year I have chosen a wooden handled grapefruit knife costing £4.95, just one of the many useful left-handed gadgets on offer.

Fiona Dickson

Didlington Manor, Didlington, Thetford, Norfolk, IP26 5AT

Tel: 01842 878673 Fax: 01842 878673

Contact: Fiona Dickson. Last orders: 12 December. No credit cards. Delivery charge: p&p extra.

Fiona Dickson's honey is particularly full bodied and richly flavoured. And if that is not enough to persuade you, there is the extra fillip of its royal connections. As well as on her own nature reserve in Didlington, she places hives in two of the Royal Parks: Windsor in the Queen Mother's garden, and Richmond in the grounds of the Royal Ballet School; and she also sells honey from Sandringham Park Estate.

Fiona is unusual in that she keeps the honey from each location separate, so each tends to have a marked character. Sandringham is quite mild, Richmond is limey, Windsor is 'heathery and chestnutty', and Didlington is 'limey and minty'. A ½lb jar costs £2.50 and a 1lb jar £3.50; or you can buy a gift of four ¼lb jars for £7.50.

Hambleden Herbs

Court Farm, Milverton, Somerset, TA4 1NF

Tel: 01823 401205 Fax: 01823 401001

Contact: Gaye Donaldson. Last orders: 17 December. Delta, MasterCard, Visa. Delivery charge: free on orders over £12.50.

If you thought that the purest, most fragrant rose water comes from the East, then think again. Hambleden Herbs sell a heavily perfumed, preservative-free, 100 per cent pure rosewater from unsprayed roses grown in Lincolnshire. A 100ml green glass bottle costs £4.50. Use it in fruit salads, ice creams, sorbets and cakes, or just splash it over your face to wake you up in the morning.

Lakeland Limited
Alexander Buildings, Windermere, Cumbria, LA23 1BQ
Tel: 015394 88100 Fax: 015394 88300
Last orders: 17 December. Switch, MasterCard, Visa. Delivery charge: for orders up to £35, £2.50 p&p; over £35, carriage free.

Good Grips really are the most comfortable-to-hold and easy-to-use kitchen tools, designed in the USA with thick black Santoprene (a rubber-like material) handles. Arthritic hands can hold and use them, and style freaks will admire them just for the sheer practicality of their design. The range includes a vegetable peeler that 'floats over potatoes', at £3.55, and a zester at £3.95.

Machiavelli
83 Kinnerton Street, London, SW1X 8ED
Tel: 0171 259 5761 Fax: 0171 259 5780
Contact: Ninai Zarach. Last orders: 12 December. No credit cards. Delivery charge: p&p extra.

If you pop a £3.20 jar of porcini mushroom fresh pasta sauce into a friend's stocking, you will be doing them a real favour. Made by Crema Lombardi, a small Italian company, it is rich and creamy with a great taste of the mushrooms and cheese (it contains both parmesan and pecorino). Available from Machiavelli (or ring them for stockists), this is one ready-made sauce no food lover could complain about.

Morel Bros, Cobbett and Son Ltd
Unit 7, 129 Coldharbour Lane, London SE5 9NY
Tel: 0171 346 0046 Fax: 0171 346 0033 email: info@morel.co.uk
Contact: David Bernstein. Last orders: 15 December. Switch, MasterCard, Visa, Amex. Delivery charge: p&p extra.

Morel Bros, Cobbett & Son specialise in mail order of fine foods from all around the world, all year round. From northern Greece comes a deep, dark red saffron with a pungent aroma. Harvested by hand from the village Krokos (Greek for crocus) where saffron has been grown for 300 years, the filaments are sorted from the petals and placed on silk-lined trays to dry. Further sorting separates the superior red from the yellow filaments, and it is these which Morel sell: either in 1g boxes of filaments costing £2.95 or as four 0.25g sachets of saffron powder costing £2.40.

Natural Collection
Friends of the Earth, PO Box 2111, Bath, Avon, BA1 2ZQ
Tel: 01225 442288 Fax: 01225 469673
Last orders: 11 December. Delta, MasterCard, Visa. Delivery charge: On orders under £5, £1.25; £5–100, £3.50.

A vegetable brush might not seem a very sexy present, but every cook needs one. Friends of the Earth Natural Collection sells a very practical one, costing £3.75, that fits neatly into the hand. It has the added advantage of being made from sustainably produced beech, with half soft Mexican White bristles for the easier jobs and half tough Bassine, a fibre produced from a rainforest vine, for tougher really dirty vegetables.

Presents from £5 to £10

Wendy Brandon
Felin Wen, Boncath, Pembrokeshire, SA37 OJR
Tel: 01239 841568 Fax: 01239 841746
Contact: Wendy Brandon. Last orders: 15 December. MasterCard, Visa. Delivery charge: £5.75 for any size order.

Although not a great fan of marmalades, I make an exception when it comes to Wendy Brandon's. Using ordinary – as oppose to Seville – oranges, hers are imbued with a deep taste of the fruit and are neither too sweet nor too sharp.

In the 'red label' (for traditional preserves made with sugar) range are some wild combinations. Try the grapefruit and juniper berries, or pink grapefruit with bitters, lime and lemon, or lime with Tequila. If you prefer a more traditional approach, there is orange with whisky or orange with brandy; made this time with concentrated apple juice. Finally there is a deep dark orange marmalade made with molasses and copious quantities of dark rum. Packed in 340g jars, the marmalades range in price from £3.20 to £3.40.

Denny's
1 Cleeve Court, Cleeve Road, Leatherhead, Surrey, KT22 7NN
Tel: 01372 377904 Fax: 01372 362920 email: dennys@btinternet.com
Contact: Nicholas Jubert. Last orders: 9 December. Switch, MasterCard, Visa, Amex. Delivery charge: p&p extra up to a maximum of £3.50.

One of the best Christmas presents I ever gave my food-loving friends was a personalised pinnie. Denny's, who incidentally has just opened a new retail shop at 55a Dean Street, London W1, runs an incredibly efficient mail-order service from Leatherhead. You must allow at least ten days, but all you need do is choose an apron (the best value is a heavy duty white cotton one at £5.05) and order up the embroidery. This comes in a choice of three styles of lettering – Script, Block and Schoolbook – and eight colours – black, royal (blue), green, red, white, navy, gold or wine. £3.50 will secure embroidery up to 30 letters about three-quarters of an inch high, centred on the bib (you can have the letters larger, but that will cost extra). There are other – and more expensive - aprons with pockets, even chefs' jackets from £10.50; but if you go for the cheapest option, you can give a really original and personal present for a mere £8.55.

The Hambledon Gallery
40–44 Salisbury Street, Blandford, Dorset, DT11 7PR
Tel: 01258 454884 Fax: 01258 454225
Contact: Victoria Suffield. Last orders: 17 December. MasterCard, Visa. Delivery charge: £3.50.

One of the most useful kitchen presents I have ever been given is an acrylic recipe-book holder. It stops food from being dropped onto the book while cooking, and it makes the recipe far easier to follow. All you do is open the cookery book at the right page, slot it between parts of the holder and there it is: propped up for you to follow. Available at £7.95.

Lakeland Limited
Alexander Buildings, Windermere, Cumbria, LA23 1BQ
Tel: 015394 88100 Fax: 015394 88300
Last orders: 17 December. Switch, MasterCard, Visa. Delivery charge: for orders up to £35, £2.50 p&p; over £35, carriage free.

The catalogue from Lakeland Limited is full of goodies for the food lover, at competitive prices. Highly desirable is the Pepperball costing £8.50. It looks like a plastic ball in bright primary colours, and you simply squeeze the pair of levers or 'ears' on top and out comes coarsely ground pepper. It is far simpler than grinding away. And to go with it there is a 100g sack of Parameswaran's Special Wynad pepper, costing £1.98. Grown in the Wynad plateau of Kerala in India, it is, according to *The Times* cookery writer Frances Bissell, the best pepper she has ever tasted.

Loftus Editions

The Hayloft, Big House Farm, Norton Lindsey, Warwickshire, CV35 8JE

Tel: 01926 843313 Fax: 01926 403636

Last orders: 15 November. No credit cards. Delivery charge: prices include p&p

The recipe organiser is designed for everyone with problems trying to keeping track of favourite recipes, whether from a cookery book or clipped from a magazine or newspaper. For £6.99 you get a pack of 60 pages (with room for 120 recipes), designed to fit into a standard 172mm x 95mm personal organiser or filofax. The pages are printed with headings for the recipe name, where you saw it, its ingredients, method, preparation and cooking times and any personal adjustments. Once you have filled it in you will always have a record with you. When shopping, you are so organised you will know exactly what to buy; and when you get home you will know exactly what to cook.

Ocean Home Shopping Ltd Trading

Unit 5, Pensbury Street, London, SW8 4TL

Tel: 0800 132985 Fax: 0171 498 8898

Last orders: 20 December. Switch, Delta, MasterCard, Visa, Amex, Diners. Delivery charge: p&p extra.

Seriously stylish are the silver-plated wine stoppers from Ocean Home Shopping Ltd, with four shapes to choose from. Most practical are the decorative ball or flat topped stoppers with tapered ends. These fit snugly into the neck of virtually any size of bottle, from very narrow to wide, and so will certainly keep wine fresh for a few days. Each stopper cost £9.95, and the good news is that for an extra £1.50 Ocean will gift wrap them – or indeed anything else you choose from its catalogue.

Replica Food Ltd

Block G, Carkers Lane, 53–79 Highgate Road, London NW5 1TL

Tel: 0171 485 3485 Fax: 0171 485 3484

home page: http://www.replica.co.uk

Contact: Andrew Senior. Last orders: 1 December. Switch, Delta, MasterCard, Visa. Delivery charge: p&p extra.

Replica Food Ltd produces the most amazing collection of plastic foods. From a boar's head complete with tusks lying on a mound of peaches and prunes to a somewhat suggestive salami, they are just what food lovers should find in their stocking (or on the pillow). Actually, the above mentioned boar's head costs £183.30 – far too much for a joke – and anyway, no-one in their right mind would even consider having it in their home. Instead, go for a selection of four dinky canapés, made on mini toasts spread with cream cheese and prawns, and an artful scattering of Danish lumpfish roe. Starting at £9.17 for the four, they are truly wonderful.

Gifts from the Grange

The Grange, Hafod Farm, Goytre, Port Talbot SA13 2YR

Tel: 0990 502206 Fax: 01639 895114

Switch, Delta, MasterCard, Visa. Last orders 7 December. Delivery charge: £2.95 for orders up to £30.00, £3.95 for up to £65.00, above that free.

A box of twenty-four traditional apples individually wrapped in tissue paper is a gem of a present for a food lover. I should know, as I have given them to favoured friends for years and they always ask for more. Ripened to perfection for eating over the holidays, the apples chosen are old-fashioned varieties such as the gloriously creamy Orleans Reinette, the nutty Cox's Orange Pippin and Ashmead's Kernal with its pear-drop flavour.

Here, however, I must declare an interest. As everyone really does enjoy them, I am featuring them in my Food Lovers' Choice. This is a small range of some of my favourite foods, put together with the above mail order company. It also includes another treat, a teeth-crunching, pure butter treacle toffee, set in tray, with a hammer for cracking it - at a mere £3.95.

Presents from £10 to £20

The Art of Eating

Box 242, Peacham, Vermont 05862, USA

Tel: (800) 495 3944 Fax: (802) 592 3400 email: circ@artofeating.com

Contact: Edward Behr. Last orders: n/a. MasterCard, Visa, Amex. Delivery charge: price includes p&p.

The Art of Eating is a quarterly newsletter owned and exclusively written by Edward Behr. It is for serious food lovers who really want to know about their food. It rarely contains recipes but rather highly opinionated, tautly written discussions about a certain ingredient or a certain area and its produce (Edward Behr does get to travel in Europe a fair bit, so it maybe Barcelona one issue, Tuscany another). If I have made it sound dull, forgive me, because I cannot tell you how thrilled I am when I see my copy plopping through the letter box. I know I am in for a riveting read. A year's subscription costs $30 (about £18).

Brogdale Orchards

Brogdale Road, Faversham, Kent, ME13 8XZ
Tel: 01795 535286 Fax: 01795 531710
Contact: Ben Harris. Last orders: 5 December. Visa. Delivery charge: p&p extra.

Brogdale Horticultural Trust boasts what is probably the world's largest collection of temperate fruits, with around 2,300 distinct apple varieties in its orchards. You can order a year-old maiden tree for £11.00, grafted from the collection. At this time of the year they usually have about 100 different varieties in stock, including such old-fashioned favourites as Ashmead's Kernal with its aniseed flavour, or Ribston Pippin. But if someone wants a particular or rare variety they will, provided they hold a tree in the orchard, graft it especially for you. As these are young trees, you will have to exercise patience as, depending on what root-stock the tree comes from, it may take up to four years before you even see an apple.

The Clark Trading Company

Freepost (Lon1083), London, SE12 8BR
Tel: 0181 297 9937 Fax: 0181 297 9993
Contact: Colin Clark. Last orders: 15 December. Switch, Delta, MasterCard, Visa. Delivery charge: £3.95 p&p; for orders over £75, carriage free.

The Clark Trading Company imports all number of goodies from the Continent, and a quick trawl through its catalogue will reveal sparkling gems to satisfy any food lover (see also page 159). A favourite from Colin Clark are *pepperoni farciti* from Franco Roi, whose superb olive oil also comes highly recommended (see page 183). These are little medium-hot red peppers about the size of cherry tomatoes that are hollowed out, stuffed with anchovy and a whole caper, and bottled in a mixture of wine vinegar and extra-virgin olive oil. As Colin eulogises: 'They are simply exquisite, there is no other word for it. The combination of flavours explodes in the mouth: not too hot but enough to produce a tingle, the slight bite of the anchovy and caper blending with the smooth olive oil and vinegar – it's all too much.' With such a commendation, £12 for a 200g jar containing ten to twelve peppers seems a small price to pay.

The Cook's Bookshop

118 West Bow, Grassmarket, Edinburgh, EH1 2HH
Tel: 0131 226 4445 Fax: 0131 226 4449
Contact: Clarissa Dickson Wright. Last orders: 21 December. MasterCard, Visa, Amex. Delivery charge: p&p extra.

Most cooks appreciate a good cookery book for Christmas. For the best advice visit – or telephone – one of Britain's two cookery bookshops. They are both piled high to the ceiling with just about every cookery book published here and all over the world, and will send them anywhere you want.

Clarissa Dickson Wright (yes, she of Two Fat Ladies fame) runs The Cook's Bookshop in Edinburgh. When she is not filming or rushing around the country, Clarissa is more than prepared to pronounce her opinion on the relative value of any cookery tome, and if you smile sweetly she will sign a copy of her latest book, *Two Fat Ladies Ride Again* (Ebury Press). In London there is Books for Cooks, 4 Blenheim Crescent, W11 1NN (Tel: 0171 221 1992, Fax: 0171 221 1517).

This Christmas promises some very interesting new books. Top of my list are Josceline Dimbleby's *Complete Cookbook* (HarperCollins), a collection of 200 recipes from the *Sunday Telegraph*; and Nigel Slater's *Real Cooking* (Michael Joseph), in which the writer departs from fast food to take a slower, while still simple, view of cooking.

Divertimenti (Mail Order) Ltd

PO Box 6611, London, SW6 6XU

Tel: 0171 386 9911 Fax: 0171 386 9393

Last orders: 15 December. Switch, Delta, MasterCard, Visa. Delivery charge: £3.95 per order.

The Divertimenti mail-order catalogue really is aimed at 'people who love to cook'. From their well chosen and extensive *batterie de cuisine* I want as a present the 'state-of-the-art' bulb baster costing £14.95. And if you have ever grappled with an old-fashioned one, you will know why. This has a soft grip, easy-squeeze handle and two interchangeable nozzle tips – one for basting and one for skimming stocks and soups. It makes cooking so much easier.

The Heritage Seed Library

Ryton Organic Gardens, Ryton-on-Dunsmore, Coventry, Warwickshire, CV8 3LG

Tel: 01203 303517 Fax: 01203 639229 email: rog@hdra.org.uk

Contact: Bob Sherman. Last orders: n/a. Visa. Delivery charge: price includes p&p.

The Heritage Seed Library offers the chance to grow and taste a bit of history while actively taking part in conservation. £16 secures a year's membership (reduced to £8 for existing members of the Henry Doubleday Research Association), and you receive copies of the newsletter *Seed News* throughout the year, plus the chance to choose six packets of rare vegetable seeds for growing in the garden, not otherwise commercially available. Choose from such glorious sounding varieties as Magnum Bonum, an old-fashioned garden pea with large scented flowers and a great flavour; Red Elephant, a large red carrot; or Lazy Housewife, a climbing French bean. Once you have joined up, you have the added bonus of swapping seeds with other enthusiasts, so you will probably never be satisfied with modern hybrid seeds again.

La Fromagerie

30 Highbury Park, Highbury, London, N5 2AA

Tel: 0171 359 7440 Fax: 0171 359 7440

Contact: Patricia Michelson. Last orders: 7 December. Switch, Delta, MasterCard, Visa, Amex. Delivery charge: p&p extra.

No one in their right mind would dream of giving a loaf of sliced white as a present; but a loaf from Poilane is more than acceptable. Lionel Poilane (there are two brothers, both bakers and locked in fierce competition) has a fine reputation for his dense, chewy and crusty sourdough. As it lasts for at least two weeks it is sent all over the world, and La Fromagerie imports it here, selling huge round loaves weighing around 2kg for £8.80. For Christmas, these are festively decorated with grapes and vine leaves in dough, with Merry Christmas or Joyeux Noël (should you want an authentic French version) written on top, and cost £17.60. And if you give them at least two weeks' notice, they can also arrange to have a friend's name included.

Mycologue

47 Spencer Rise, Kentish Town, London NW5 1AR

Tel: 0171 485 7063 Fax: 0171 284 4058

Contact: Martin Lewy. Last orders: 17 December. No credit cards. Delivery charge: prices include p&p.

Just as every cook needs at least one good knife, so does a mushroom hunter. Mycologue supplies all manner of equipment, guides and accessories for mushroom-philes. Their Italian collecting knife, costing £14.75, has not only a good sharp steel blade for cutting stalks but also a serrated edge for scraping off the earth and a brush on the end for light cleaning of the gills. This is vital because, as every good mushroom hunter will tell you, you should lightly clean your mushrooms before you put them in the basket, otherwise they will be full of grit. There is also a de-luxe version at £19.25, which comes complete with compass (in case you get carried away while picking) and belt sheath.

Pilton Manor Vineyard
Pilton, Shepton Mallet, Somerset, BA4 4BE
Tel: 01749 890325 Fax: 01749 890262
Contact: Jim Dowling. Last orders: 10 December. MasterCard, Visa. Prices include p&p.

Fresh out of the barrel this year, for the first time ever, you can buy a British brandy. A single cask brandy, it was distilled from an unchaptalised, unsulphured base wine made in 1991, and then 'ferreted away under bond for five years to mature in oak barrels'. It is classily presented in a long slender bottle with a charming, understated label. One brandy expert, I hear, has described it as 'pretty'; and while laying no claims to being a connoisseur myself, I found it rather agreeable, relatively smooth and deep. With only 891 bottles currently on sale (and I have one), and another two barrels almost ready for bottling to make around 2,000 bottles in total, a 35cl bottle costs £17.99. If it is, perhaps, a trifle on the expensive side, I would think it worth it for its curiosity value and, of course, rarity.

R E Campbell Ltd
69 Maltings Place, Bagley's Lane, London SW6 2BY
Tel: 0171 371 5566 Fax: 0171 371 5676
Contact: Bob Campbell. Last orders: 16 December. No credit cards. Delivery charge: £8 minimum charge.

For sheer indulgence, it is difficult to beat a fresh truffle. R E Campbell imports *Tuber melanosporum*, the dark black truffle from Perigord with a great smell and a great taste. At £400 a kilo, you may be surprised to hear that a 30g truffle – the size of a walnut – only costs around £12. And if you really want to spoil a food lover, pack it in a kilner jar with some risotto rice and a few eggs. After a couple of days they will have picked up the truffle's heavily perfume so you can eke out the pleasures in store.

Stephanie Fernald Ceramic Designs
10 Longley Road, Rochester, Kent, ME1 2HD
Tel: 01634 401427 Fax: 01634 401427
Contact: Stephanie Fernald. Last orders: 1 December. No credit cards. Delivery charge: p&p included.

Plates – or rather, what you serve your food on – can be a matter of great concern to a food lover. Do you opt for a plain, simple style and go for unadorned white so as not to detract from the food, or do you heap on the colour or patterns? I favour a somewhat eclectic approach, mixing old and new and plain white with blue and white, and the odd dash of other colours to add further excitement. But then I love my table to look really busy.

Stephanie Fernald makes wonderful bone china, screen-printed with great restraint and elegance. From her classical collection comes a 27cm dinner plate decorated with early ornate eating implements in black and white, costing £19.50. It would blend with most china, and a single plate can be used to serve cheese or a pudding. On the other hand, you never know; you might want to start a whole collection.

Olive Oil

A good extra-virgin olive oil – one with character and flavour – is essential to the well-stocked kitchen. Indeed no food lover can ever have too many in the cupboard, provided of course they do not leave them mouldering so long they turn rancid.

Judy Ridgway, author of the estimable *Olive Oil Companion* (Little, Brown) writes: 'The style of an olive oil can vary from the very sweet and very mild to the very bitter and pungent and you also have to take its pepperiness into account. There is no right and wrong in the styles of [olive] oil. It is all simply a matter of personal preference. For example, punchy, peppery oils have no intrinsic value over lighter oils. However there may well be a culinary difference. Very strong oils will kill the flavour of delicate foods and light oils will not be discernible in stronger dishes.... [It] is not just a cooking medium, it is also a flavouring ingredient in its own right. Thus you may want a particular type of flavour to match or contrast with the food being dressed or cooked in oil.'

I asked Judy, as an expert, to choose three of her favourite olive oils, all with different personalities. Here is her list with tasting notes.

Nunez de Prado comes from Baena in Spain, and has been made by the same family since 1795. The aroma is full of fruit with lemons, apples, melons, passion fruit and bananas jostling for place. The taste is just as good, with the same exotically fruity flavour. There is only a touch of pepper with a lovely smooth, sweet aftertaste. A 500ml bottles costs £8.25 from the Oil Merchant (Tel: 0181 740 1335)

Possenti Castelli, an Italian olive oil from near Rocca San Zenone in the Umbrian hills, has a strong fruity aroma with plenty of mown grass and salad leaves. The flavour is sweet and fulsome with medium pepper. It is an elegant oil, costing £18.55 for a litre or £10.80 for 500ml from the Oil Merchant.

Roi is an organic oil from the hills behind Taggia in western Liguria in Italy. It has a very attractive light almond aroma, with apples and a touch of grassiness. The flavour is sweet and nutty, with light pepper and a little tart bitterness on the aftertaste. This is a very smooth, delicately complex and versatile oil, available from Take It from Here (Tel: 0800 137064) and costing £10 for a 500ml bottle.

Presents from £20 to £50

Beverly Hills Bakery

23 Egerton Terrace, Knightsbridge, London SW3 2BX

Tel: 0171 584 4401 Fax: 0171 584 1106

Contact: Mark Peterson. Last orders: 15 December. MasterCard, Visa, Amex. Delivery charge: prices include p&p.

Beverley Hills bakes 'real' American muffins. Real muffins, according to owner Mark Peterson, means 'a good full-blown top. And if it's cracked, that's OK. All it means is the mixture has overflowed on top, we like it that way in the States. A muffin's texture must be fairly light and when you squeeze it, fairly soft'.

They will deliver their muffins, baked every morning, anywhere in London in a gift basket in a range of sizes starting at £25 for 27 pieces. Out of town, they send them in a tin costing £37 for 38 pieces. Flavours include cranberry, a seasonal mincemeat ('like a mince pie only a muffin'), blueberry, double chocolate, lemon, honey bran and pecan orange. You can choose your own selection of flavours and either order all muffins or have a couple of all-American cookies and brownies thrown in for good measure.

The Chocolate Society

Claypit Lane, Roecliffe, Borough Bridge, Yorkshire, YO5 9LS

Tel: 01423 322230 Fax: 01423 322253

Contact: Nicola Porter. Last orders: 17 December. Switch, Delta, MasterCard, Visa. Delivery charge: £2.50 for up to 1kg: £5 for any weight over 1kg.

For £50 you can join up a friend to the Chocolate Society for a year. And provided they really do like chocolates and take up all the 'benefits', they will certainly get their money's worth. Every member is issued with £120 of vouchers which includes £20 to spend at the Chocolate Society Shop at 36 Elizabeth Street, London SW1 (see page 89), £20 off wines to drink while eating chocolates, £20 discount off any cookery book bought at the Cook's Bookshop (see page 179), a bi-annual newsletter, and invitations to various events and tastings. And to top all that, you get a further 5 per cent discount on all chocolates you buy from them during the year.

David Mellor Mail Order

4 Sloane Square, London, SW1W 8EE

Tel: 0171 730 4259 Fax: 0171 730 7240

Last orders: 18 December. MasterCard, Visa. Delivery charge: £3.50 in the UK.

David Mellor is known for his choice of stylish utensils, gadgets and cutlery, and no food lover could fail to find something in his catalogue. This year, I have got my eye on the Alessi kitchen timer, costing £25.90. Designed by 'post-modernist maestro' Michael Graves, in stainless steel and brightly coloured red or blue plastic, it looks superb with its rounded wings. Equally importantly, like any piece of really good design, it works.

The Gluttonous Gardener

82 Wandsworth Bridge Road, London, SW6 2TF

Tel: 0171 371 0775 Fax: 0171 371 8324

Contact: Ned Trier. Last Orders: 19 December. Switch, Delta, MasterCard, Visa. Delivery charge: standard £6.

The Gluttonous Gardener sends out present kits based on a simple but sound idea. 'For the same price as a bouquet of flowers,' says Ned Trier, 'you can give something that will give immediate enjoyment to a food lover and if looked after properly will last for ever'.

The Olive Enthusiast's Kit fits that description neatly. For £25 you get a bushy young olive tree about one foot high, planted in a terracotta pot. If you protect it from the frosts (Ned sends out complete care and harvesting instructions), within a couple of years you should harvest a few olives and, a couple of years later, enough to fill a jar. For immediate consumption there is an estate-bottled extra-virgin organic Spanish olive oil, and the whole kit comes attractively presented in a wooden crate. Other presents, also costing £25, are the Currant Affair – a blackcurrant bush and a bottle of crème de cassis; and the Wine and Vine Box – a vine and a bottle of claret.

Paul Heathcote's Cookery Classes

Paul Heathcote's Restaurant, 104–106 Higher Road, Longridge, Preston, Lancashire, PR3 3SY

Tel: 01772 784969 Fax: 01772 785713

Contact: Andrew Lee. Switch, Delta, MasterCard, Visa, Amex, Diners.

Everyone loves to watch chefs cooking; there is always so much to learn. Paul Heathcote, star of the north, is one of the most approachable chefs I have ever met, and £40 secures a place on his day courses. These run throughout the year and cover such topics as Roasting and Simple Saucing, Simply Fish Dishes and (before Christmas) Party and Christmas Cooking. You arrive at 10 am, spend the morning watching Paul, and then sit down to a glass of champagne and a three-course lunch in his two-star restaurant. For dates and further details of the days out, contact Andrew Lee.

Sent a Scent

Jo Malone Ltd, The Old Imperial Laundry, Warriner Gardens, London, SW11 4XW

Tel: 0171 720 0202 Fax: 0171 720 0277 email: info@jomalone.co.uk

Last orders: 18 December. Switch, MasterCard, Visa. Delivery charge: £3.50 for one item, £5 for two or more.

Jo Malone scents are pure heaven, and visitors to her shop at 154 Walton Street in London cannot but feel totally pampered. Her collection of fragrances, bath oils and body lotions are designed to be used with each other, and by combining – or layering – them you can create a new and highly individual scent identity.

Food lovers will particularly adore the clear, refreshing Grapefruit, made from 'oil of grapefruit obtained from the fruit peel of the Citrus Paradisi tree, combined with top notes of lemon and tangerine and a drydown of vetyver'; Nutmeg and Ginger, with its heady warm spiciness; or the 'sensuous citrus notes' of Lime, Basil and Mandarin. Prices start at £13.95 for a 100ml small travel bath oil or body lotion, with a two-bottle fragrance combining set costing £33.50. And if you cannot go to the shop in person, she runs a Sent a Scent service from The Old Imperial Laundry.

Silver Direct

PO Box 925, Shaftesbury, Dorset, SP7 9RA

Tel: 01747 855844 Fax: 01747 854700

Contact: Nicki Coleman. *Last orders: 19 December. Switch, Delta, MasterCard, Visa, Amex. Delivery charge: prices include p&p.*

Freshly ground pepper can perk up even the dullest of meals. No true food snob would ever dream of setting off on a holiday – whether trekking in the Himalayas or sun-bathing in Ibiza – without their own personal pepper-mill. Silver Direct sells a tiny silver-plated model costing £40. Only 2¾ inches high, it still takes enough peppercorns for several meals, and as it comes in a green leather case it fits neatly into a breast pocket or handbag. On the other hand, you could opt for the silver version from Asprey, which will set you back £115.

Taste of the Wild

31 London Stone Estate, Broughton Street, London, SW8 3QJ

Tel: 0171 498 5654 Fax: 0171 498 5419

Contact: Alistair Lomax. *Last orders: 19 December. MasterCard, Visa, Amex, Diners. Delivery charge: carriage free for orders in Central London and over £100; otherwise £10 per order; minimum order £20.*

A packet of something special is always a joy for a food lover. Taste of the Wild has an enticing range of seven dried wild foods, each one with a recipe by Michel Roux of Le Gavroche printed on the back. These include 15g of the tiniest dried morels (the British, apparently, prefer them small), with his recipe for chicken breast in a rich morel sauce, costing £4; or 100g of wild rice (actually a grass harvested from the lakeland shores of Minnesota) costing £1.99 that Michel suggests turning into a pilaff with pecan nuts and raisins. The others are 100g of pine kernels 'extracted by hand from pine cones'; 80g of dried forest mushrooms, a 'medley of seasonal forest favourites'comprising 30g of porcini, 30g of trompettes de la mort and 20g of shi-itake. The sum of £25 will secure the whole range, gift boxed and sold under the dubious title of Roux'd Food.

The Tasty Mushroom Partnership

Poppy Cottage, Station Road, Burnham Market, Norfolk, PE31 8HA

Tel: 01328 738841 Fax: 01328 738841

Contact: Peter Jordan. Last orders: n/a. No credit cards.

Fancy foraging for mushrooms, but worried about what to pick? Peter Jordan of the Tasty Mushroom Partnership organises days out all over the country, from Scotland to Wales, the Midlands, East Anglia and the Home Counties. In a group limited to no more than 15, he will guide you to the right species, give hints on where to look and how to pick them, and check over your basket before you go home. Forays take place from 24 August right through to the beginning of November, and cost £25. Peter issues gift vouchers to secure a place for 1998.

Toxique

6 Green Street, Bath, Avon, BA1 2JY

Tel: 01225 318004 Fax: 01225 447317

Contact: Adam Hatcher. Last orders: 12 December. Switch, Delta, MasterCard, Visa, Amex, Diners. Delivery charge: around £6 depending on weight.

Normally I do not go for gift baskets of food. They do not strike me as offering good value (you can usually put the same selection together for half the price), the food is often unimaginative and of poor quality, and the presentation a bit 'twee'. But Toxique could be the exception that proves the rule.

Its round or square Shaker-style boxes are in frightfully good taste, and are filled with 'authentic' ingredients. Each box costs £24.99 and is themed. The Vegetarian box is packed with tomato and basil pesto, hot spicy coriander, and tarragon and orange mustard (all made in the kitchens of their restaurant in Melksham), bags of black eye and mung beans, Puy lentils, wild rice, cous cous, packets of sunflower and pumpkin seeds, wakame seaweed, plus a couple of recipes telling you how to use the ingredients together. Other themed boxes include Japanese, Indian, Thai and English Breakfast.

Presents from £50 to £100

De Gustibus

A and D Food, Pakenham, Park Lane, Witney, Oxfordshire, OX8 8JU
Tel: 01235 555777 email: dan_bagelman@msn.com
Contact: Dan Schickentanz. Last orders: n/a. No credit cards.

For anyone who wants to improve their baking, what could be better than a present of a bread-making course?

Dan Schickentanz of De Gustibus runs Saturday courses throughout the year from his bakery in Witney. You turn up at 9 am for coffee, tea and breads (aprons and work materials provided, but it is suggested you wear anti-slip shoes or trainers), then are bombarded with all sorts of fascinating technical information until lunch-time. After that, you roll up your shirt sleeves and get kneading and baking until going-home time late in the afternoon. A fascinating day, and even the most novice bread-maker can grasp the basics. As Dan says, 'once you know the mechanics of bread-making and can bake a simple bread – you're on your way'. A day's baking with Dan is limited to 15 people at a time, and costs £85. Contact him for further information about dates.

Leavens Above! is a longer but equally intensive affair that stretches over a whole weekend in Melmerby, Cumbria. The two-day course, which includes one night's B&B accommodation and meals, is £250. For this you get to work with Andrew Whitley of the Village Bakery (see page 78), see his famous wood-burning ovens, and eat in his restaurant; but most of the tuition is under the aegis of Paul Merry, an Australian baker who builds brick ovens as a sideline.

Elizabeth Eaton

58 Abbey Street, Faversham, Kent, ME13 7BN
Tel: 0171 730 2262 Fax: 0171 730 7294
Contact: Ros Hartmann. Last orders: 15 December. Switch, MasterCard, Visa. Delivery charge: p&p extra.

Sometimes the simplest things cost an outrageous fortune. And even if £84.50 does seem a horrendous amount of money for a stripped willow cheese cloche with tray, it does not make it any less covetable. Made in France (no doubt by an impoverished basket maker), it epitomises rustic chic and would lend an elegance to even the most mundane of cheeses. This highly desirable item (well, to me at least) will allow your cheeses to breathe while protecting them from the flies. If you prefer to view it first, pop into the Elizabeth Eaton shop at 85 Bourne Street, London SW1 8HF.

Glazebrook & Co

PO Box 1563, London SW6 3XD

Tel: 0171 731 7135 Fax: 0171 371 5434

Contact: Jonathan Glazebrook. Last orders: 4 December. MasterCard, Visa. Delivery charge: p&p extra.

Style guru Stephen Bayley has very decided opinions when it comes to cutlery. 'All technologies moderate human behaviour. In that respect a fork is no different from an interactive multi-media console. A three-tine (prong) fork dictates a very particular style of eating. Fine for delicate peas, less good for a haunch of bloody venison.'

Whether you believe him or not, there is no denying that the three-tine fork and the accompanying curved pistol knife with the flat butter-spreading blade have become *ne plus ultra* of the cutlery world. Glazebrook & Co sells a stainless steel version with a mirror finish that would do any table proud. A five-piece place setting – three-prong table and dessert forks, dessert spoon, pistol table and dessert knives – costs £29.20, so starting with enough for two will set you back £58.40. If all you want are the table forks and knives, these cost £4.70 and £7.80 respectively.

Meg Rivers Cakes

Middle Tysoe, Warwickshire, CV35 OSE

Tel: 01295 688101 Fax: 01295 680799

Contact: Meg Rivers. Last orders: n/a. Switch , Delta, MasterCard, Visa. Delivery charge: prices include p&p.

There are book clubs, CD clubs, so why not a cake club? Every cake lover would be thrilled to be given a membership with a year's subscription costing £92. Run by Meg Rivers (see page 84), the club's members receive six cakes a year plus a cake storage tin with their first cake.

Meg's cakes are made with the very best natural ingredients: raw sugar, organic flour, local free-range eggs and English butter. 'If I use alcohol – rum, brandy or kirsch – that's what I pour in. I don't use any essences. Unbleached white flour is organically produced, and the dried fruits are the best money can buy.' Baking powder has been banished; 'you don't need it if you cream the butter properly.'

The cakes arrive for the first weekend of every other month, and apparently members plan tea parties around them. Each cake weighs around 1kg, and changes to suit the season and time of year. Starting in February, last year's members received a Madeira cake, then an apricot and almond cake in April, pineapple in June, cherry in August, chocolate in October and a rich fruit Christmas in December.

Student Survival Service

Scottish Gourmet, Freepost, Thistle Mill, Biggar, ML12 6BR

Tel: 0500 340 640

Contact: Gillian Bell. Last orders: n/a. Switch, MasterCard, Visa, Amex, Diners. Delivery charge: prices include p&p.

Do you have children, grandchildren, nieces or nephews at college or university? And are you worried they are not eating properly? Then the Student Survival Service would make a perfect present. For £89.85, they deliver three food parcels a term that will ensure no student need starve – all for around £1 a day. A typical monthly parcel will include two portions of freshly made soup, fresh pasta sauce, beef stir fry, stovies (a Scottish dish of potatoes, meat stock and onions), and vegetable casserole,as well as bacon, sausages, cheese, biscuits and marmalade. There is a vegetarian option with everything freshly made in the Scottish Gourmet kitchens (see page 23). Ingredients and dishes are of extremely good quality and only need re-heating or a quick cook in the microwave; and to prove they have thought of everything, delivery at the beginning of each month during term-time is on a Wednesday: the day when traditionally most students have a half day.

Summer Isles Foods

Achiltibuie, Ullapool, Highlands and Islands, IV26 2YG

Tel: 01854 622353 Fax: 01854 622335

Contact: Keith Dunbar. Last orders: 7 December. Switch, MasterCard, Visa. Delivery charge: prices include p&p.

If you want undying gratitude from a kipper lover, join them up to the Kipper Club, run by Keith Dunbar of Summer Isles Foods. A subscription, costing £60, secures the member two pairs of exceptionally fine plump kippers – a pair weighs around 350 to 400 grams – every month. They arrive during the first week of whatever month chosen (in time for a weekend's breakfast), and keep on coming for the next five months. These are either Scottish herrings landed at the Ayrshire ports or Loch Fyne, or imported from Norway or Iceland; and Keith defies anyone – even the greatest enthusiast – to spot the difference. What he believes is critical is the oil content of the fish and the size. His herrings are brined in salt for about 30 minutes, then smoked for 18 to 24 hours, which is a good bit longer than most. As for cooking kippers, as always the simplest way is the best, so Keith grills his with a knob of butter.

Presents over £100

Val Archer
68 Salcott Road, London, SW11 6DF
Tel: 0171 350 2862 Fax: 0171 924 7258
Contact: Val Archer. Last orders: 1 December. No credit cards. Delivery charge: £10.

Val Archer's highly decorative food illustrations have adorned the pages of BBC *Good Food* magazine and the *Sunday Telegraph*, and are known for their detail, their vibrancy and the richness of their colour. Val has just published two prints in a signed limited edition of 200. 'Spring Lemons' shows a mound of piercingly yellow lemons set off by a blue and white bowl; 'Autumn Pears' are piled in a basket and surrounded by autumnal fruits, berries and nuts. Each print costs £195, or you can buy the pair for £350.

Fournos Garden Ovens Ltd
River Lodge, 40 Park Avenue, Wraysbury, Middlesex, TW19 5ET
Tel: 01784 483336 Fax: 01784 483336
Contact: Antony Marsh. Last orders: 15 November. No credit cards. Delivery charge: included in price.

The latest must-have for slavishly fashionable cooks is a *fournos*, which is Greek for wood-burning oven. If you have failed to hear about its advantages, may I remind you that the Bluebird restaurant (Sir Terence Conran's latest in Chelsea's Kings Road) and the River Café swear by theirs? And how they cook, others inevitably copy.

Antony Marsh has designed his on traditional lines based on a model discovered in a Cypriot garden, and the arched brick ovens in Welsh cottages. Constructed from 370kg of, and I quote, 'refractory, mono-lith castable concrete', it functions most efficiently outside although it can be connected to a flue in the kitchen.

Apparently best for slow-braising all those peasant dishes, you can use it for roasting, baking bread direct on the sole (floor) or even barbecuing. But all this does not come cheap. £1,500 secures delivery, installation (there is an oven stand), instructions, plus two cookery books written by Antony which must make it the biggest, heaviest and nearly the most expensive present a food lover could dream of.

Jocelyn Burton Silversmith and Goldsmith Ltd
50c Red Lion Street, London, WC1R 4PF
Tel: 0171 405 3042 Fax: 0171 831 9324
Contact: Liz Ridley. Last Orders: 31 October. No credit cards. Delivery charge: p&p extra.

This Christmas, if you can possibly afford it, go for a Burton: a Jocelyn Burton, whose work in silver is immensely covetable. As the late Jean Muir said: 'her work is beautifully made, with an innate sense of quality. She is an ultimate craftsman; without any doubt among the best silversmiths in this country. Her works are modern classics, a continuation of a wonderful line of the craft.'

In her collection there are several pieces to grace a table. A silver hive honey pot costing £1,800 is decorated with gilt bees buzzing up its side, while on top rests the queen with lapis lazuli eyes. More restrained is a silver salt cellar with the Chinese bat of happiness, again with eyes of lapis lazuli, at £587.50; and a matching spoon costing £150. She will undertake private commissions starting at £120.

Tasting Places
136 Lancaster Road, London, W11 1QU
Tel: 0171 229 7020 Fax: 0171 229 4383
Contact: Sarah Robson. Last orders: n/a. MasterCard, Visa, Amex.

Most food lovers could not imagine anything better than spending a week in an Italian country villa cooking, shopping, tasting and eating with an experienced chef. Keen to stress that these are 'cookery holidays and not basic cookery courses', Tasting Places organises weeks for around 14 pupils in such far-flung spots as La Cacciata, 'on the rambling and spacious Belcapo Estate with dramatic views of the ancient hill-top city of Orvieto', or Villa Ravida in south-west Sicily in an 18th-century villa with its own estate-bottled olive oil.

With such well-known British cooks as Alistair Little, Antony Worall-Thompson or Sophie Grigson to guide you through a week's regional cooking (and yes, you do get to cook yourself), holidays start at £925 (excluding the flight). Seems like indulgent fun to me.

Festive Decorations

For many, the month or so of Christmas festivities is a heaven-sent opportunity to decorate in an exuberant and lavish way which would be totally over the top at any other time of the year. And why not bring light, glitter or greenery into the house in the dark depths of mid-winter?

For some, decorating means dragging out of the attic a life-time's collection of multi-coloured baubles. Others agonise and plan a co-ordinated look that could be high baroque or casual country, folksy northern European, naïve New England, primitive and vivid Mexican, Shaker simplicity pared down to the elegantly Spartan, or designer-led ultra minimalist modern. The romantically inclined go for gold and glitter, silver and sparkle, swags, garlands and streaming ribbons, luscious metallics in shimmering stained glass colours, lashings of tartan, piles of pine cones and evergreen boughs, and huge bowls or baskets of spicy wintry pot-pourri.

And then there is the question of the Christmas tree. If you want to buy one direct from the growers, and need advice on how to care for it, send a stamped addressed envelope to the British Christmas Tree Growers Association, 12 Lauriston Road, Wimbledon, London, SW19 4TQ. On the other hand, you may prefer nothing more than a few contorted willow branches or even no tree at all. As for decorating, this can go from the sublime to the minimal, a strategically placed designer bauble or two, in gleaming white or matt black, with the odd gilded walnut.

There is plenty on offer through the post. Both Paperchase (0171 636 1333) and the General Trading Company (0171 730 0411) have excellent mail-order catalogues crammed with desirable Christmas goodies.

If a trip to London is part and parcel of the run up to the holidays, then you should visit Harrods, Knightsbridge, London SW1 (Tel: 0171 730 1234) whose enormous Christmas department actually opens in mid-August. Closer to the day Liberty, Regent Street, London W1 (Tel: 0171 734 1234), Heal's, 196 Tottenham Court Road, London W1 (Tel: 0171 636 1666), Habitat, 206 King's Road, London SW3 (Tel: 0171 351 1221) or Tottenham Court Road, London W1 (Tel: 0171 631 3880), the Conran Shop, 81 Fulham Road, London SW3 (Tel: 0171 589 7401), Peter Jones, Sloane Square, London SW1 (Tel: 0171 730 3434), John Lewis, Oxford Street (Tel: 0171 629 7711) and Selfridges, Oxford Street, London W1 (Tel: 0171 629 1234) all have a good selection of tree ornaments and other decorations. Smaller London boutiques such as Nice Irma's, 46 Goodge Street, London W1 (Tel: 0171 580 6921) has sparklers from India; Verandah, 15 Blenheim Crescent, London W11 (Tel: 0171 792 9289) stocks a nifty line of Mexican painted tin and other witty items; Tobias and the Angel, 66 White Hart Lane, London SW13 (Tel: 0181 296 0058) is a treasure trove for the 'country' look; Inca, 45 Elizabeth Street, London SW1 (Tel: 0171 730 7941) is the place for South American handicrafts; and Graham & Green, 4 Elgin

Crescent, London W11 (Tel: 0171 727 4594) or 164 Regent's Park Road, London NW1 (Tel: 0171 586 2960) is reliable for the tasteful and unusual. (Here I will declare an interest. I started the shop, but no longer have a connection with it). The museum shops at The V & A, Cromwell Road, London SW7 (Tel: 0171 938 8500) and the Royal Academy, Burlington House, Piccadilly, London W1 (Tel: 0171 439 7438) are also good places to find well designed Christmas cheer.

But we should not forget fresh flowers. An arrangement – seasonal or otherwise – is almost always welcome. Most florists make special Christmas decorations, anything from small table-top-sized trees or miniature topiary to fresh garlands and seasonal bouquets. For a modern style, keep a beady eye out for galvanised steel containers, brown paper and raffia for tying up in big bows. For a 'wild' look, buy - or raid the hedgerows for trails of ivy and branches of hips, haws and berries other than the ubiquitous holly. Colour co-ordinate bought flowers, or go for all-white with lusciously scented lilies or tuberoses. Whatever you do and however you decorate your house, make sure it is a welcome haven for friends and family.

American Retro

35 Old Compton Street, London W1V 5PL

Tel: 0171 734 3477 Fax: 0171 734 6885

Contact: Polly Java. Last orders: 11 December. Switch, MasterCard, Visa, Amex, Diners. Delivery charge: p&p extra.

The trend-setting shop American Retro began its life a decade ago selling American goods exclusively. Now it is better known for classy glass from Germany and Finland, nifty plastic from Germany and up-to-the-minute clothing from all over Europe. One American import they do still stock is the kitsch lover's favourites of favourites: a sublimely silly string of chilli lights costing £28. They are bright red, and shaped for all the world like the real thing. Just thread them through the branches of the Christmas tree.

Andean Alpaca

Cotehay Farm House, Brockhampton, Gloucestershire, GL54 5TH

Tel: 01242 820864 Fax: 01242 820092

Contact: Clive Walker.Last orders: 21 December. No credit cards. Delivery charge: p&p extra.

From Andean Alpaca come hand-made garlands, tree ornaments and other decorations in a choice of jolly bright red or green, or red and green checked cotton, that remind you of cuddly soft toys. A bonus is that they are unbreakable, should last forever and would be ideal in a house with inquisitive toddlers determined to explore absolutely everywhere. Mind you, these decorations are so cheery they would make anyone young at heart smile. A mixed set of 12 tree ornaments, that might include a bell, Christmas tree, a holly leaf, star, heart, teddy, cat or dog, costs £9.95. Or for the same price you could choose a string of squishy stars and hearts or bells, a garland of trees or teddies, or a large stocking for the mantelpiece. A single large bell or a large single holly sprig costs £4.95, and a cluster of bells, £10.95.

Appalachia – The Folk Art Shop

14a George Street, St Albans, Hertfordshire, AL3 4ER

Tel: 01727 836796 Fax: 101727 836920

Contact: Rosalina Dowds. Last orders: 14 December. MasterCard, Visa, Amex. Delivery charge: for orders up to £25, £2.50; £25–£40, £3.50; £40–£100, £4.50; over £100, free.

Forgive me for stating the obvious, but most everything from Appalachia – The Folk Art Shop is folksy. But, as it is imported from the USA, it is cunningly so. There is a charming wreath made from twisted grapevines with a simple painted wooden angel and star, costing £18.99. They are big on angels. There is a winsome cloth angel holding a star, designed to go on top of the tree, at £27.99; and another to hang off a branch at £10.99. Stained glass angels, each one unique, also for hanging on the tree or in a window to catch the light, cost £9.99. Other tree ornaments come in the form of patchwork shapes filled with whole cloves at £2.99. Another utterly delightful and unusual decoration is the bay and cinnamon garland with dangling felt stars and hearts, that costs £18.99. And the shop also imports the Naturals range made on a farm in Kentucky, which includes a striking dried apple and cinnamon wreath with checked bow at £17.99.

Blue Cat Toy Co.

Builders Yard, Silver Street, South Cerney, Gloucestershire, GL7 5TS

Tel: 01285 861867 Fax: 01285 862153

Contact: Mally Findlater. Last orders: 26 November. MasterCard, Visa. Delivery charge: minimum order £5, £1.50 p&p.

The Blue Cat Toy Company produces two catalogues showing their rubber stamp range. The main one has three pages of some sixty different Christmas designs in a wide range of styles, from retro to modern, and costs £2. The smaller Deco Stamps catalogue costs £1 (you can order both for £2.50). The latter illustrates their 'chunkier' stamps and is particularly seasonal. Worth ordering are a stunning sun, three different stars, a snowflake and a striking dove, with prices ranging from £2.95 to £8.90. They also supply ink pads in dye and pigment inks. Apparently the pigment inks (not recommended for use by young children) produce a more subtle, painterly effect with a light-fast, softer, more opaque image. These come in two sizes and fourteen colours, including silver, gold and copper. Also available is embossing powder. If you pour it on the stamped image while still wet, then gently heat it, the surface becomes raised and glossy.

Cera Candela

White Stones, Hill House Hill, Liphook, Hampshire, GU30 7PX

Tel: 01428 722136 Fax: 01428 722136

Contact: Lindsay Withycombe. Last orders: 26 November. No credit cards.

Delivery charge: minimum order £10; for orders up to £25 add 15 per cent for p&p; over £25, add 10 per cent.

Real beeswax candles have a captivating fragrance and a gentle, soft, golden-yellow sheen. They may be more expensive but it is worth splashing out for special occasions. Cera Candela produce hand-made candles in a wide variety of sizes. A 5-inch rolled honeycomb burns for three hours, a hand-dipped 10-inch candle flickers merrily away for ten, while a night light glows for between four and six hours. Prices start at £2.50 for a 5-inch pair, £5 for a bundle of four tied up with green paper ribbon and raffia, with a 10-inch pair costing £4.50. Cera Candela will also make to any size you want; and, on the premise that candles make welcome presents, will send them out in green gift boxes tied with red braid - but remember to allow 28 days for delivery.

The Cracker Maker

Tithe Farm, Bishampton, Nr Pershore, Worcestershire, WR10 2NE

Tel: 01386 860646 Fax: 0121 357 4312

Contact: Angela Hawkins. Last orders: 12 December. No credit cards.

Delivery charge: £3.50.

Luxurious hand-made reusable crackers in sumptuous fabrics, sold with a selection of separate gifts, seem a terrifically good idea. Customers can buy their crackers in a wide choice of Christmas red, claret, or bottle-green velvet; bright or antique gold silk; sparkling gilded hessian; co-ordinating silk and velvet from the Antique collection; or tapestry with a choice of wired antique gold rosettes, ribbons, tartan rosettes or tiny gilded seed heads. The crackers cost £5.95 each, or £39 for six in a box with 24 extra snaps. Gifts are extra and sold as packs, with six individual gifts starting at £15. These include a gentleman's tartan handkerchief, tartan key ring, wooden 'cigar' pen, three scented soap sticks tied in a pretty bundle with ribbon or flowers, a wooden scrabble timer, and emery boards in a grosgrain case. They also sell snap packs with extra fillings for future use with hats, snaps and 'anecdotes'.

To co-ordinate with the crackers are wonderfully stylish decorations. A pair of miniature terracotta pots to hold night lights or candles are trimmed with cinnamon sticks and a dainty garland of tiny natural pine cones, and cost £5.50 and £5.90 for natural or gilded finishes. Charming candle balls with seed heads, pine cones, nuts, chillies and cinnamon sticks, or floral candle balls with natural dried roses (in a choice of red, yellow, cream or magenta) or fragrant lavender and marjoram, come in three sizes starting at £9. There are decorative standard trees in terracotta pots, made from seed heads, nuts, cones or pink or green oak leaves, which come in four sizes - mini (7cm) small (9cm), medium (12cm) and large (15cm) with prices ranging from £9 to £22. There are also double candle rings, welcome rings in vine or dried oak, either natural or gilded; pine cone obelisks, hanging balls, antique bobbin candle sticks in two sizes, and chilli garlands, wired to twist around a candle, in natural, red or gilded.

Almost everything really is exceptionally pretty, and to prove the point Martha Stewart, America's Christmas queen, is featuring them in this year's edition of her magazine.

The English Stamp Company

Worth Matravers, Dorset, BH19 3JP

Tel: 01929 439117 Fax: 01929 439150

Contact: Jan Sibthorpe. Last orders: 19 December. Switch, Delta, MasterCard, Visa, Amex, Diners. Delivery charge: p&p included.

Rubber stamps are far and away the easiest way to put a pattern on almost anything that could do with a little seasonal cheer. Cards and gift tags are just the beginning: fabrics, wood, and even walls can be stamped. And once you start it can become quite addictive.

Stamps from the English Stamp Company are often hand cut, and the stamping process results in images with an attractive, slightly rough and ready but fashionably 'broken' surface. They produce several Christmas stamp designs, from holly, doves and Christmas trees to Christmas bells, three kings and a dove carrying mistletoe, in a range of sizes with prices starting at £3.50 for a 1-inch stamp. Water-based stamp paints come in a choice of twelve colours as well as festive gold and silver, at £2.95 and £3.50 respectively. They also put together a Christmas stamp kit at £18.95 that includes a choice of two 2-inch stamps or one 4-inch stamp, plus a 60ml pot of gold paint (or any colour you specify), an applicator and full stamping instructions. There are more than 70 designs to choose from, seasonal and otherwise, and the English Stamp Company will custom-make stamps to your design costing between £19.95 for a 5-inch to £49.95 for a 10-inch stamp. You should allow at least ten days for its delivery.

Hambleden Herbs

Court Farm, Milverton, Somerset, TA4 1NF

Tel: 01823 401205 Fax: 01823 401001

Contact: Gaye Donaldson. Last orders: 17 December. Delta, MasterCard, Visa. Delivery charge: free on orders over £12.50.

If you have ever felt tempted to make your own pomanders but never been sure how to do it, Hambleden Herbs sell an orange pomander mix. Made from ground cinnamon, cloves, allspice, nutmeg and orris root, a 200g bag costs £2.50 and is enough for six oranges. All you do is stud the oranges with cloves and pierce them all over the skin with a fine needle. Then put them in a bowl covering them with the pomander mix. Turn them every so often so they are covered in the mix, and leave them for about one month. When they are suitably hard and scented, tie them up with ribbon and they are ready for hanging around the house or on the Christmas tree. Also for scenting the home are the packets of 20g each of frankincense and myrrh at £1.75. As they are gently heated, they release a pungent aroma.

Most of the products from Hambleden Herbs are organic (grown to Soil Association standards). Tempting either for eating or stringing up as decorations are the organic Chilli Braids at £12.50 each. Made with cayennes, the bumpy, cardinal red chillis, 'they are grown and plaited by a man called Joe whom we met in California. Each braid has about 30 chillies between 5 and 8 inches'.

Hardy's

Crown Point, Waterside, Ely, Cambridgeshire, CB7 4AU

Tel: 01353 664432 Fax: 01353 663371

Contact: Caroline McCleave. Last orders: 6 December. No credit cards. Delivery charge: p&p extra.

Devoted fans of Hardy's Christmas pot-pourri have delightedly reported back to Caroline McCleave that, a year later, the fragrance still lasts. It is a most extravagant, luxurious and heady mix of spice, wood and fruit that will make you imagine you have been transported to a pine forest to drink mulled wine. It smells intoxicating and looks simply amazing, with whole cinnamon sticks, pine cones of all sizes, pieces of bark, a gilded pomegranate, dried orange slices and split lime. A 1kg cellophane bag tied with a gold bow costs £35, and will fill a good-sized basket and scent an entire room. There's a smaller bag at £10. New this year are small bottles of refresher oil at £4, and 4-inch gilded candles set in gold long-Tom flowers that release the same opulent seasonal scent and cost £9.50.

Heart of Europe Trading

5 Baronsmead Road, London, SW13 9RR

Tel: 0181 286 6187 Fax: 0181 255 0175

email: euroheart@compuserve.com

Contact: Caroline Degen. Last orders: 15 December. No credit cards. Delivery charge: p&p extra, charged at cost.

Lucky German *kinder* get stocking fillers every day of the month on the run up to Christmas. Little sacks or stockings numbered from one to twenty-four are filled with a treat and hung up for the children to open every morning when they wake up. Heart of Europe Trading imports a variety of these Advent 'calendars' from Germany, ranging from numbered fabric sacks mounted on a highly decorated appliqué fabric, to small hessian stockings trimmed with red and green, with a red string for hanging. Prices start at £12.99, but these must be ordered by 1 November to make sure they arrive in time. For actual Christmas decorations, they also import other typically German Christmas angels, ornaments and various knicknacks, and I suggest you ask for their illustrated folder so you can have a browse through.

Helen Porter Decoupage

Parc-Y-Justice, Llanilterne, Cardiff, CF5 6JH

Tel: 01222 890652

Contact: Helen Porter. Last orders: 30 November. No credit cards. Delivery charge: large parcels £6.50 for next-day delivery; smaller items p&p extra.

Helen Porter does beautiful decoupage with flowers, fruit and feathers on a large variety of practical objects. For Christmas this year, she has created two designs for place mats and coasters that would look very smart on the festive board. Using hexagonal mats with a dark green background, one design combines holly berries, mistletoe and ivy; and the other has bright red poinsettias and holly sprigs. Both cost £7 for a table mat and £2.50 for a coaster. With many other designs and colours available, for use either at Christmas or throughout they year, Helen will also work to commission. Together you could come up with your very own exclusive design.

K D Richards Ltd

Richards House, Gateway, Crewe, Cheshire, CW1 6YY

Tel: 01270 211311 Fax: 01270 256356

Contact: Kenneth Hecht. Last orders: 21 December. MasterCard, Visa. Delivery charge: £1.95 per order.

K D Richards is a serious supplier to the trade of festive glitter in the way of lace, bows, fabric, gilded grapes, silver leaves, candle rings, gold and silver sprays, willow wreaths and rings. Although the company is a wholesaler, it will deal with private customers. So if you cater for crowds during the season and are inclined to decorate on an equally lavish scale, leaving no visible object unadorned, this is the place to order from in bulk.

It also stocks a collection of wired ribbons called Elegant Metallics for presents or decorating the tree. (One year, I covered my tree with nothing but shimmering silver bows, and very effective it was too.) The ribbons come in all sorts of extravagant shining finishes, including solid gold Chemise, a woven gold and silver see-through mesh, checks in burgundy and gold, gold or ivory, and tartans in red and green, navy and hunter (green), and burgundy all threaded with gold. And if you cannot tie a decent looking bow, you would be wise to invest in the DecoFun English Bow and Decoration Maker. This costs £6.99, comes fully assembled with 'no heavy or splintery wooden parts', and apparently makes tying bows a doddle. The company also stocks the gorgeous Nature's Own range of wrapping paper and co-ordinating ribbons, for elegantly wrapped parcels.

Naif Ideas

Fox Cottage, West Street, Kingham, Chipping Norton, Oxfordshire, OX7 6YQ

Tel: 01608 658028 Fax: 01608 658028

Contact: Penelope Menato. Last orders: 7 December. No credit cards.

Delivery charge: p&p extra.

Checked or tartan fabric dollies, or garlands of stars and hearts filled with pot-pourri, have great charm and a refreshing simplicity. Designed and made by Penelope Menato herself, these are decorations with humour and innovation. Instead of a garland, why not hang a welcoming doll on the front door? Dressed in a red tartan dress with red and white striped legs, it holds a wooden sign saying 'We still believe in Christmas'. Or, instead of a fairy, there is a dainty 'Fairy Bunny' dressed in a white net skirt and mohair pullover at £14, to grace the top of the tree. For perching on the mantelpiece choose between a doll holding a star at £13 or a large calico reindeer with a bright red bobble nose at £16. There are also patchwork star and heart garlands costing £11, and just a heart garland at £10. For hanging around the house there are large single hearts or stars at £3.80, and a small tartan angel with raffia wings at £4.50.

Nantucket New England Crafts
PO Box 233, St Albans, Hertfordshire, AL3 4DT
Tel: 01727 845770 Fax: 01727 857373
Contact: Deborah Lambert. Last orders: 21 December. MasterCard, Visa.
Delivery charge: p&p extra.

Nantucket New England Crafts imports all manner of hand-made decorations from New England. Over there, Christmas is taken very seriously; houses are lavishly decorated and scented for the season and celebrations take place with great gusto. Here you can get clever perfumed swags of dried sliced apple rings and pomegranates strung with cinnamon sticks, whole nutmegs, walnuts and bay leaves, tied up top and bottom with checked gingham. These arrive complete with a phial of fragrance to scent a room, and come in two sizes: 9 inch at £8.95 and 14 inch at £11.95. They also import beeswax tree decorations tinted a bright cranberry red, in various shapes such a teddy, rocking horse, angel, candle, holly leaf, and even a Santa Claus. These cost between £3 and £10. What is particularly clever is that they are scented with cinnamon and the fragrance is slowly released as they are warmed by the heat of the tree lights.

Panduro Hobby
Freepost, Transport Avenue, Brentford, Middlesex, TW8 8BR
Tel: 01392 427788 Fax: 0181 847 5073
Diners. Last orders: 9 December. Switch, Delta, MasterCard, Visa, Amex,
Delivery charge: minimum order £20; for orders under £50, £2.95 p&p, plus £1.50 handling charge.

The enormous Panduro Hobby catalogue has more than 90 pages devoted to Christmas-related items imported from Sweden, where Christmas is big business.

There are dozens of kits for the crafty to assemble that include candle holders and candle-making equipment (Scandinavians adore candles), nativity figures, advent calendars and tree ornaments. There is also plenty for the less nimble-fingered to choose from. Ribbons, wrapping paper, hand-dipped Swedish candles, charming tiny hand-painted wooden tree ornaments, an unpeeled willow star to decorate yourself, straw wreaths, straw ornaments, table mats, paper napkins, a jolly child's Christmas apron, transfers, stickers, gift bags - in short just about everything you can imagine that can be given a seasonal Swedish twist.

Pene Dene Flowers

Sigwells, Sherborne, Dorset, DT9 4LN

Tel: 01963 220460

Contact: Pene Dene. Last orders: 15 November. No credit cards. Delivery charge: p&p extra.

Pene (pronounced Penny) Dene is something of a wizard with silk flowers. She imports possibly the best range in the country from mainland China, the Philippines and Thailand, but she stresses that they are 'not made in sweat-shops'.

Pene will make up almost anything. At Christmas she makes abundant cascades, starting at £13.50 for a one-foot length. Made with artificial fluffy fruit with a delicate bloom, berries, and her striking flowers, these can be hung on walls or laid on the table, two arranged back to back, with a candle in the middle as a marvellous centre-piece. She also makes glorious swags with artificial fir and grey-coloured leaves with fruit and flowers, starting at £12 per foot. In fact Pene prefers to make to order, so you can have any length, any colours and any varieties of fruits, flowers or berries you want. And if you store her decorations carefully, they should last for several seasons.

Penkridge Ceramics

Bott Lane, Walsall, West Midlands, WS1 2JJ

Tel: 01922 25181 Fax: 01922 722449

Contact: Nicky Smart. Last orders: 21 November. No credit cards. Delivery charge: minimum £3.50 p&p

A selection of the extensive range of life-size, perfectly modelled and coloured ceramic fruit and vegetables, convincing enough to fool the eye, made by Penkridge Ceramics, now come in white. These bleached versions are exceptionally elegant and stylish. Choose from whole Bramley, Cox, Golden Delicious or Granny Smith–shaped apples, Conference, William or Comice-shaped pears, or sliced halves, either single or bunched bananas, peaches, lemons, pomegranates, prickly pears, starfruit, figs, plums, quinces, tamarillos, melons, and baby or large pineapples. Prices range from £8.50 to £150 for the largest pineapple. Arrange a selection in a bowl with gold or silver balls, evergreen leaves and gorgeous ribbons, and you will have a most original Christmas centrepiece.

Quartet Food & Wine

23 Market Place, Henley on Thames, Oxfordshire, RG9 2AA
Tel: 01491 412128 Fax: 01491 412098
Contact: Judy Ruback. Last orders: 12 December. Switch, Delta, MasterCard, Visa, Amex. Delivery charge: p&p extra.

Dedicated food lovers make sure there are plenty of edible decorations hanging on the Christmas tree to nibble when feeling peckish. Just about every chocolate shop stocks up with brightly – if not garishly – coloured foil-wrapped chocolate shapes that can be almost anything from fish to Father Christmas faces.

Far more restrained are the miniature Christmas puddings from Quartet Food & Wine. Packed in single acetate cube boxes tied up with gold looped thread , these are two-bite-size puddings made from a rich, dark fruit cake rolled with brandy into the appropriate shape. With a lick of white chocolate on top, and decorated with tiny sugar-paste holly leaves and berries, they look for all the world like the real thing. A single pudding boxed costs £1.25, or you can buy them in a gift box of six for £5.99. Last Christmas, I went to a tea party where these puddings were arranged on a large plate. They looked irresistible. Should you want to serve them, you can buy them 'loose' at 45p each; but you will have to buy at least 100 and discuss the most practical means of delivery when ordering.

If you are worried about the quality of the chocolate in your tree decorations, then I suggest you apply to the Chocolate Society, Clay Pit Lane, Roecliffe, Borough Bridge, Yorkshire, YO5 9LS (Tel: 01423 322230, Fax: 01423 322253) for their boxed Father Christmas. Made with their superb milk, dark or white chocolate (see also page 89), these are about 4 inches high, cost £6.99 and put most cheap novelties in the shade.

Renwick & Clarke

190 Ebury Street, Mozart Terrace, London, SW1W 8UP
Tel: 0171 730 8913 Fax: 0171 730 4508
Last orders: 13 December. Switch, Delta, MasterCard,Visa, Amex. Delivery charge: p&p extra.

In Victorian times it was thought rather witty to dip real walnuts in silver and mix them in a bowl with plain, unadorned ones. Renwick & Clarke have gone one better. First they make a resin cast, then silver plate their nuts. Choose from walnuts, peanuts, almonds or chestnuts at £8.70 each, or hazelnuts at £5.60 each. You need no more than a few to make an effect, and they are shown off to their best advantage if you mix them with plain nuts and display them in a glass bowl.

Sarah Cavendish Designs

Benham Grange, Halfway, Newbury, Berkshire, RG20 8NE

Tel: 01488 658985 Fax: 01488 658755

Contact: Sarah Cavendish. Last orders: 25 November. No credit cards. Delivery charge: around £5, depending on order.

Sarah Cavendish's hand-painted free-form interlocking jig-saw table mats won an award for the most innovative product at the British Craft Trade Fair in 1994. Her work is most unusual and original, and she takes the place mat out of the ordinary into the rarefied. She also makes more traditional square Christmas place mats, based on a design of a wreath on a red background by stencillist and paint specialist Belinda Ballantine. A 10 x 10-inch mat costs £10, and they go up in size to 14 x 12 inches. Should you want your own design, either for yourself or to give as a present, Sarah is more than happy to undertake the commission. She charge £5 for a 4 x 4-inch mock-up, which will be deducted from the order if the pattern suits.

Shaker

25 Harcourt Street, London, W1H 1DT

Tel: 0171 724 7672 Fax: 0171 724 6640

Contact: Sarah Richards. Last orders: 14 December. No credit cards. Delivery charge: minimum £5.50.

While not specifically Christmassy, neither the rosemary-and-grapefruit-scented squat round candle nestling in the plain and quiet simplicity of a wooden Shaker box at £19.95, nor or the 8-inch tapered beeswax candles packed in an oval box at £32.95, would be out of place during the holidays. Especially if, in the Shaker tradition, the other table decorations are simple and sparingly elegant. Why not use the boxes as containers on the table and fill them with evergreens, the odd sprig of holly, rosemary, bay leaves or a bunch of mistletoe tied with green garden twine? Then twist strands of fresh ivy so they meander down the centre of the table and around the candles, and strategically place pine cones to complement the natural wood of the boxes.

The Stamping Ground

PO Box 1364, London W5 5ZH

Tel: 0181 758 8629 Fax: 0181 758 8647

Contact: Rosemary Jackson. Last orders: 12 December. MasterCard, Visa. Delivery charge: £1.50 p&p.

The Stamping Ground has a small but choice selection of stamps grouped together in categories called 'marine', 'gothic', 'country' and 'baroque'. Designed with interior decoration in mind, with a little flair and imagination several could be utilised for a seasonal sensation. With prices ranging from £7.95 to £9.50, in particular there are three different-shaped stars all measuring 3 inches; a cherub in two sizes (3 inch and 4½inch) complete with a trumpet, a 4½-inch winged cherub, and a 3-inch ivy leaf. While it's not particularly seasonal, dog lovers should note the fine 3-inch Scottie.

Toby Abrehart Frames

46 High Street, Wrentham, Suffolk, NR34 7HB

Tel: 01502 675394

Contact: Toby Abrehart. Last orders: 17 December. No credit cards. Delivery charge: p&p extra.

Master guilder and custom frame maker Toby Abrehart has been gilding leaves for two years now, and often adds them to his exceptional hand-made frames. He uses Dutch metal, a dead ringer for gold, on any leaves he can find: oak, maple, ivy, chestnut, tulip tree, red oak. Then he waxes and 'antiques' them, which also prevents them from tarnishing. They cost £1 each and a collection would look extremely glamorous scattered around the Christmas dinner table, artfully arranged on a chimney piece or even tucked under the ribbon on a special gift. But you probably need quite a few to make a show. They are reasonably fragile, but if treated with care should last for years. If you have a special leaf in mind, give Toby plenty of time; otherwise take pot luck, as he usually has gilded leaves in stock .

The Tole Candle Company

PO Box 36, Battle, East Sussex, TN33 0ZS

Tel: 01424 775708 Fax: 01424 775545

Contact: Tine Desoutter. Last Orders: 20 December. No credit cards. Delivery charge: £3.50 per order.

Candlelight can be even more seductive and flattering if softened with a decorative shade. Pierced metal ones are particularly appealing: they not only catch and reflect the light but are also safer and longer-lasting than paper shades. The Tole Candle Company has a very attractive selection in antique brass, pewter, verdigris or silver, costing £15, and plain brass at £14. It also sells charming brass or silver night light holders at £9, with the shade punched in a pattern of stars and Christmas trees. Another speciality is the aluminium everlasting candle. Based on a Victorian original, it has a fibreglass wick inside a candle-shaped metal container that holds the smokeless, odourless lamp oil. Refillable, it will burn for up to six hours and comes in a 9-inch standard size costing £19.95 for a pair, or an 11-inch church size costing £23.50 a pair, in a choice of dark green, burgundy, gold, blue, black or ivory. Also worth looking at are the various candlesticks, candle bases, and a plain but elegant extending wall bracket that takes a single candle.

Toppers International Ltd

7 Acacia Park, Bisghop's Cleeve, Cheltenham, Gloucestershire, GL52 4WH

Tel: 01242 676288 Fax: 01242 676288

Contact: Gabriella Burgess. Last orders: 31 October. MasterCard. Delivery charge: orders up to £85, £3.50 p&p; over £85, p&p free.

The elaborate tablecloths, place mats and napkins from Toppers International Ltd combine traditional needlecraft skills with modern fibres for easy care. Designed by Gabriella Burgess and made in the Far East, the cloths are meticulously hand-machine embroidered, appliquéed or cut-worked.

Christmas Damask, with elegant delicate holly, is the most subtle and formally elegant; but more casual designs such as Goose with Holly, Baby Angel, Blue Holly, Bows and Stars, and Regency Damask in burgundy or bottle green, would be perfect for a Christmas celebration. The patterns are striking and unusual, and some of the non-Christmas designs such as the hand-painted Grapes, white Giant Rope with thin tracings of gold on the tassel, or vivid autumnal Royal Leaves, also have a seasonal feel. Even though these linens look labour intensive, they are in fact made of superior poly-cotton and are machine washable, providing the temperature is kept at 50 to 60 degrees to keep the poly fibres supple. Most of the designs come in a choice of 36-inch and 54-inch square, and 54 x 72-inch and 54 x 90-inch rectangular; but custom sizes can be ordered. Prices range from £4.95–£5.95 for 18-inch square napkins, to £5.95–£7.95 for oval place mats, and £29.95–£79.95 for the tablecloths.

Tree Fellows

106 Askew Road, London, W12 9BL

Tel: 0973 821039

Contact: Jo Boggan. Last orders: 22 December. No credit cards. Delivery charge: included in price.

Christmas tree decorator extraordinary Jo Boggan, whose corporate clients include such big names as the National Gallery and the Science Museum, will go anywhere to create a fabulous Christmas tree. While her corporate clients want 'high impact' and tend to go for themes (she once created a forest with 15 trees), most of her private customers prefer a less formal look and on the whole are 'a little more traditional'. Some choose their trees 'really glitzy', others go for the 'homely' look; but last year her Mexican tree with little sacks of beans, corn cobs and lots of dried chilli peppers proved popular with everyone.

If you baulk at the expense and sheer indulgence of hiring a tree decorator, you could still benefit from Jo's ideas. She thinks for instance that any tree – a traditional evergreen or even a birch – looks fantastic sprayed with ultra-violet paint and lit with UV lights so 'it really glows in the dark'. If you do decide to indulge, a Tree Fellows custom-decorated tree costs £25 a foot (plus travel expenses outside London). Delivered and decorated in situ, it also includes - joy of joys - removal after Twelfth Night, to be ecologically disposed of and recycled.

V V Rouleaux

10 Symons Street, London SW3 2TJ

Tel: 0171 730 3125 Fax: 0171 730 3468

Contact: Annabel Lewis. Last orders: 18 December. Switch, Delta, MasterCard, Visa, Amex. Delivery charge: p&p extra.

From the beginning of October V V Rouleaux will have its Christmas ribbons in stock in their shop, London's ribbon haven. Imported from all over the world, there are hundreds to choose from in gold or silver wired mesh, velvets, damasks, plain satins or embossed with stars, snowflakes, Santa Claus or fleur-de-lys, with prices starting at around £1.50 per metre. With no catalogue as such, ordering by phone can be difficult. But if you think you know what kind of ribbon you want (or even if you do not) ring them up and discuss the details. They will then send off samples and you start from there.